awaken

To my sons Seth and Caleb.

With all of my heart, I long for you to know the beauty of prayer. Prayer changes everything! It unlocks a world of wonder and awe—a world where you learn to hear God's voice and feel His love for you. Prayer takes you into a deep adventure unlike any other. I want you to know how to access this precious and private place. I am writing this prayer planner for you and future generations and perhaps even my own. Consider it a map that will guide you to the greatest treasure you will ever discover.
I love you both with all of my heart. - Mami

To my husband Eloy.

Eloy, thank you for believing, pastoring, loving, counseling, encouraging, and challenging me! This book is a byproduct of your AMAZING love and dedication. Let's keep discovering what other crazy good things God has planned for us!
Te amo.

My Prayer Planner

Fervent.
Intentional.
Prayer.

BY: ALINE MARIN

THIS PRAYER PLANNER BELONGS TO:

....

THE LORD GOD HAS GIVEN ME
THE TONGUE OF THOSE WHO ARE
TAUGHT, THAT I MAY KNOW HOW TO
SUSTAIN WITH A WORD HIM WHO IS
WEARY. MORNING BY MORNING HE
AWAKENS; HE AWAKENS MY EAR
TO HEAR AS THOSE WHO ARE
TAUGHT.

Isaiah 50:4 (esv)

How to use it!

The Monthly Guide

The heart of My Prayer Planner is the Monthly Guides. Each month you will begin a new guide that covers seven key areas of your life. Ask and wait on God to reveal fresh details or directions on how to pray for each area. Then use the guide as a point of reference throughout the month. At the end of each guide, you will find "Prayer Request & Thank You!" pages. On the prayer request page, you can add any extra requests that come up throughout the month. The thank-you page is provided to help cultivate a daily habit of gratitude. Each monthly guide includes a "Monthly Prayer Goal" sheet. Here you will find a section to copy your monthly memory verse, along with a place to jot down any words of encouragement or direction that you are sensing for the month. You will also see a place to write any lies, shame, or guilt you may be dealing with and the truth to replace them, and lastly, a gauge to help you identify areas that you may need to focus on for that particular month.

Scriptures to Pray

Praying scripture is a powerful weapon! The more we know and pray God's word, the more we pray His will.

Here you will find scriptures to pray over your mind, will, relationships, identity, government, leaders, and more. Use the scriptures provided in this section to help you declare His word over your life throughout the year.

Dr. Mark Jones

"The Surrender Prayer" & "The 40 Day Worship Challenge" were written by my dear friend and mentor, Dr. Mark Jones, who is the Author of the book, Unscripted: Discovering Authentic Intimacy with God through the 40 day Worship Challenge. He is currently the Prayer Pastor at Mannahouse Church in Portland, Oregon. Eloy and I are blessed to call him and his lovely wife, Susan, our Pastors and friends. Thank you, Pastors, for allowing me to share this with our readers. You are a beacon of hope that is always pointing us to Jesus!
For more information, please visit www.first15am.org or order the book via Amazon.com.

Awakenings

In this new edition, we are introducing twelve awakenings. Simply put, these are twelve verses and drawings that align with the vision and theme of the prayer planner. We hope the illustrations inspire deeper meditation into the meaning of each verse. My prayer is that each awakening would create an awareness of his presence. I want to thank our dear friend Rhuan Carneiro for contributing his beautiful drawings and graphic design.

The goal for each month is to memorize and meditate on the monthly verse and be transformed the renewal of our minds. Romans 12:2

Knowing God's Voice

Knowing God's voice is our right, privilege, and responsibility as children of God. In 2017, I faced an extremely difficult battle against postpartum depression. It was in the midst of this horrible valley that I discovered the beautiful voice of a loving Father. John 10:3-5 (NLT) says: *"The gatekeeper opens the gate for him, and the sheep recognize his voice and come to him. He calls his own sheep by name and leads them out. After he has gathered his own flock, he walks ahead of them, and they follow him because they know his voice. They won't follow a stranger; they will run from him because they don't know his voice."* There is nothing more frightening than feeling lost, confused, and abandoned! I have discovered that Satan will do anything he can to drown out the voice of the Holy Spirit. He knows that once we hear God's voice for ourselves, we will awaken to the reality that we are not alone. We will be reminded that "greater is He that is in us than he that is in the world!" Satan will bombard us with lies for as long as we let him, but God promises us in James 4:8 that if we draw near to Him, he will draw near to us. Knowing God's voice is crucial to our journey as Christians because God continues to speak today, and He has input for our everyday life. We, His sheep, should be able to recognize His voice. The more we practice praying, listening, and obeying, the easier it becomes to identify when He speaks.

Our central scripture for this planner is Isaiah 50:4 (ESV): *"The Lord God has given me the tongue of those who are taught, that I may know how to sustain with a word him who is weary. Morning by morning he awakens; he awakens my ear to hear as those who are taught. The Lord God has opened my ear, and I was not rebellious; I turned not backward."* Recognizing God's voice is something that is taught by the Holy Spirit and takes time to develop through intimacy in prayer, the studying of His Word, and stepping out in faith. The number one thing we need to do is to show up morning after morning and surrender our will over to His. He is the one who awakens our ear.

So what does God's voice sound like?
• It sounds like the Bible because the Bible is His word. (Rom. 10:17)
• It inspires and stirs us to do what is right. (John 14:26)
• It never makes us feel ashamed. (Romans 5:5-9 ampc)
• It sounds like an invitation. (Rev. 3:20)

The Five Witnesses

The Five Witnesses is a simple guide passed down to me by my dear friend Art Johansen, who received it from Pastor Dick Iverson. Art was an elder at Mannahouse Church and served faithfully throughout his lifetime. In 2020 we celebrated his homegoing, and though we miss him deeply, his love for Jesus and His house remains alive in us today. Wisdom would say that I ought to pass this guide along to you.

The Guidelines

In Art's words, this is not a fail-proof method. It's solely a guide. I should note that this isn't a guide for everyday choices. Instead, it is for big decisions like; relocating to a new city, changing jobs, getting married, buying a house, etc. If you have two to three of the 'five witnesses,' you can move forward with more confidence as you step out in faith. Keep in mind that they don't have to be in this specific order. Also, note that in the last two witnesses, you are dealing with people. Sometimes people can make mistakes. So, it is good to have multiple prophetic words or more than one counselor. A good example of how to use the five witnesses would be; if you had three prophetic words but no peace in your heart, you may want to wait.

The Five Witnesses

1. Is it biblically sound?
2. Do your circumstances align?
3. Do you have peace in your heart? (Col. 3:15)
4. What are the people who counsel you saying? For example, parents, spouse pastors, therapists, mentors, friends. (Pro. 15:22)
5. Do you have one or more prophetic words regarding this decision?

What if you don't "hear" anything? What if it feels like God is silent? I love how Art explained this to us. The bible says in Isaiah 30:21, "Your ears will hear a word behind you, "This is the way, walk in it," whenever you turn to the right or to the left." If you don't hear God, then maybe you are on the right path. Keep going. You may not need to change course because perhaps you are headed in the right direction!

Trusting God

In the book *Keep Your Love On: Connection Communication and Boundaries* author Danny Silk does a wonderful job at presenting The Trust Cycle. Research has shown that infants must go through what is called the 'trust cycle' many times in order to develop a sense of safety, love, and a healthy bond with their parent/caregiver. I believe that It is a great example of how our trust in God the Father grows when we pray. Prayer provides a wonderful opportunity for God to show His love, care, and faithfulness towards us. Let's do as the Bible encourages, "worry about nothing, but instead pray about everything."(Phil. 4:6) Prayerfully consider your areas of need. Take time to write down your prayer request in the monthly prayer guides. On the Prayer Request page you can create a sense of expectancy by filling in the date requested, and then watch for His response and note the date answered. Nothing is too small for God. So don't hesitate about praying over the seemingly "small things."

What does the cycle look like?

1. You become aware of a need.
2. You voice your need to God in prayer.
3. God meets your need.
4. Your trust in God grows.

When have you seen the Trust Cycle in action in your life?

What was a need that you voiced to God?

....
....
....

How did God meet that need?

....
....
....

How did your trust in God grow?

....
....
....

I PRAY THAT FROM HIS GLORIOUS, UNLIMITED RESOURCES HE WILL EMPOWER YOU WITH INNER STRENGTH THROUGH HIS SPIRIT. THEN CHRIST WILL MAKE HIS HOME IN YOUR HEARTS AS YOU TRUST IN HIM. YOUR ROOTS WILL GROW DOWN INTO GOD'S LOVE AND KEEP YOU STRONG. AND MAY YOU HAVE THE POWER TO UNDERSTAND, AS ALL GOD'S PEOPLE SHOULD, HOW WIDE, HOW LONG, HOW HIGH, AND HOW DEEP HIS LOVE IS. MAY YOU EXPERIENCE THE LOVE OF CHRIST, THOUGH IT IS TOO GREAT TO UNDERSTAND FULLY. THEN YOU WILL BE MADE COMPLETE WITH ALL THE FULLNESS OF LIFE AND POWER THAT COMES FROM GOD.

Ephesians 3:20 (nlt)

The 40 Day Worship Challenge!

BY: DR. MARK JONES

*Rise early, before the sun is up; I cry out for
help and put my hope in your words. Psalms 119:147t*

Devotions will be defined as "time alone with God."

The challenge will be to give God the first 15 minutes of your day (Matt. 6:33) for the next 40 days.

Practically, what does this look like?

Set Time:

The first thing you want to do is get a vision to meet with God daily. Note that this time will be the most resisted activity on the planet. The enemy does not want you to spend intimate quality time with God. The reason is because God is the source of all life. Your connection to Him is vital! The enemy knows this and tries to keep us from spending quality time with God. That is why we are going to give Him the first. The first is the best and we are giving that time to Him.

Set Plan:

Start each day in God's presence surrendering your will to His (Rom. 12:1). Worship is the greatest act of intimacy on the planet. It is to know God in the inner man (Ps. 46:10). Each day was meant to be a new encounter with Father God (Eph. 2:18; Romans 8:15) through our Lord Jesus Christ. You were made able, by the blood of Jesus, to enter into the Holy of Holies and commune with God on a moment to moment basis. The greatest gift Jesus provided was access (Heb. 4:16) which was the purpose of the Cross. You were given access to God through the blood of Jesus. His sacrifice made a way for each of us to enter in and enjoy God's Presence once again. That is why in John 14:6, Jesus said, "I am the way the truth and the life, and no man can come to the Father except by me." Jesus is our only access. Jesus made a way by paying the ultimate price for our sins. We can worship the Creator now "in spirit and in truth" (John 4:24). All else in life pales in comparison to the fact we can enter into an ongoing intimate relationship with the Creator of the Universe.

Let's get started! Create a Survive-and-Thrive Kit...
Your Survive-and-Thrive Kit is made up of your Bible, a devotional, a source of music, some headphones, a journal and a pen. Begin by committing an amount of time you want to spend with Him. Fifteen minutes is a good place to start. Continue for the next 40 days.

Set Place:
Pick the place where you are going to meet. Choose a comfortable place where you feel relaxed and where you will not be disturbed. This place should be free from distractions so that you can focus all your thoughts on the Lord. This might be in your home or at another location. You decide. Wherever you can get alone with God and open up your heart to the flow of His love will work perfectly. The purpose of this time with God is to encounter His love for you and for you to express your love back to Him (Ps. 27:8, Ps. 143:8). In this place you are going to connect heart to heart with your Creator. Use worship music to help set the mood and train your heart and mind to focus. Focus is a key to spending time alone with God. Hebrews 12:1 tells us to fix our eyes on Jesus.

The principle of FOCUS will be your aim in the first moments of the encounter as you quiet yourself before Him (Ps. 62:1).

Fix your gaze... Hebrews 12:2
Open your heart... Revelation 3:20a
Connect your spirit... 1 Corinthians 2:10-12
Usher in His presence... Revelation 3:20b
Start the flow... John 7:38

Free church ready resources available at www.first15am.org

The Surrender Prayer

BY: DR. MARK JONES

I. FATHER

Heavenly Father, good morning! Thank You for this New Day! This morning I'm choosing, with excitement and anticipation, to surrender my heart (mind, will, and emotions) to Your Unfailing Love (Ps.143:8)! I'm offering myself (my body, soul, heart and spirit) as a living sacrifice to You, recognizing it's the blood of Jesus that allows me to do this (Rom.12:1; Eph.2:18). Help me to quiet my heart before You (Ps.62:1) and receive Your Love. Father God, You are my fortress and my shield (Ps.46:1) and my hiding place today (Col.3:3; Pr.18:10)!

My life is hidden in You (Col.3:3)! Thank You that I am always welcome and can run to You for safety (Pr.18:10). I am focusing now on all the things that are in heaven (Col.3:1). I'm coming boldly into Your Presence as You've instructed me to do, asking You for grace and mercy to help me today(Heb.4:16).

Your grace and love fills me, surrounds me and protects me (Ps.46:1). Thank You for supplying my daily bread (Luke11:2-3), whichI know is sufficient for me. You are everything to me! Thank You for satisfying my deepest needs (Phil.4:19); no one else can. Your Unfailing Love is better than life itself (Ps.63:3)! I want you to know that no matter what happens to me today, You are enough and I will praise You (Hab.3:17-19) with all my heart.

Father God, I trust You! Thank You for holding me in Your arms (Ps.68:19) which is my place of rest and safety. I am responding to Your love right now (Ps.27:7-8). Today I choose to humble myself under Your mighty hand (Js.5:8). Please teach me Your ways (Is.55:8) and reveal Your heart to me (Jer.33:3). Thank You for being my Father (Rom.8:15) and for Fathering me (Rom. 8:15). I open up my heart to Your Love right now.

The Surrender Prayer

BY: DR. MARK JONES

II. SON

Jesus, thank You for caring so deeply for me that You would sacrifice Yourself on the Cross for me. I fix my gaze on You today knowing that You are the author and finisher of my life of faith (Heb.12:2) and I open my heart to You today (Rev.3:20). You are my Savior and Lord! I surrender my heart to you! Thank You that I am seated with You in heaven (Eph.2:6). That's amazing! Please help me today to see the things I face from Your perspective. Today I am casting all my regrets, worries and fears on You (1Peter5:7). Please forgive me and cleanse me from all wrong thoughts, feelings and actions as right now I'm choosing to forgive those who have offended or hurt me. I'm choosing now to forgive them, release them and bless them (Matt.7:1-3). Thank You! Forgive me for judging and being critical of others (Matt.7:1-3). Please produce in me a genuine love for those I contact today. Please open my heart to Your heart of compassion and concern for others. I choose to trust You in all circumstances and situations (Pr.3:5-6). Help me not to grumble or complain about anything today (Phil.2:14) or compare myself to others (2Cor.12:9).

Apart from You I realize and confess, I can do nothing (John15:5), but declare the truth that through You all things are possible (Mark9:23). In me, let Your purposes be done today on earth as it is in heaven (Matt.6:10). In my weakness I stir my faith that You can move mountains in my life and in the lives of those around me (Mark11:23). You are the Mountain Mover! I confess that nothing, little or big, is impossible with You (Luke1:37). Thank You for all you are, all you've done and are going to do. You are the same yesterday, today and forever (Heb.13:8). Thank You for all You have provided for my life. (Ps.100:4). I choose to be grateful today (Phil.4:6). I am declaring, this is a day You have made to rejoice and be happy in You(Ps.118:4; Phil.4:4; 1 Thess.5:16)! I recognize that in You I live and move and have my purpose for living (Acts17:28). I confess today that my life is not my own for You have purchased me with such a great price (1Cor.6:19). I willingly surrender today to You gracious love.

My confession this morning is this (Ps.143:8; Pr.3:5-6)(Gal.5:5-6):

Jesus, I trust You!

Jesus, I love You!

Jesus, I need Your help!

The Surrender Prayer

BY: DR. MARK JONES

III. HOLY SPIRIT

Thank You Holy Spirit for leading and guiding me today. Please breathe on me afresh today. Thank You for delivering me from the evil one (Matt. 6:13) and all the temptations that are lurking both in me and around me (Col. 3:5). Alert me to any carnal urges that come into my mind today and help me to immediately refocus my thinking onto You (Rom. 8:12; Phil. 4:8). Train me to ask for Your specific help in every situation I face. I recognize my greatest enemy is my own ego, pride, and self-will. Keep me from self-promoting or becoming discouraged today.

Please convict me when I try to lead my own life. Please help me return to trusting You (Prov. 3:5-6) by confessing I trust You. Thank You for Your promise that I can hear your voice (John 10:27). Teach me to respond immediately. Holy Spirit please help me to hear and see what you are saying and showing me today (Mark 4:9; Luke 10:23). Help my eyes and ears be clear and my heart be clean today. Please open my ears to Your voice and my eyes to see Your visions. Teach me to listen to Your still small voice in the midst of all the other noises (1Kings 9:11-13). Help me to discern clearly what you are saying. Help me to respond to Your voice and carry out the Father's will today!

Let the Bible come alive today! Please activate inside of me the precious gifts I've been given. Please reveal to me what spiritual and natural gifts I have and continually train me how to use them (Ps. 18:32-35). Thank You for being my mentor, coach, and friend (John 15:26) and for guiding me continually. I want to depend on You more and more as I learn to walk closer to You.

Place upon me today the full armor of God that I might fight the good fight of faith (Eph. 6:9-12) every moment today. Keep me in the tension of your purposes and securely on the path that has been chosen for me (Ecc. 6:10). Please help me not to stray and wander off course. Help me to move forward into Your perfect will today. Help me not to look back, but only forward; no regretting (Phil. 3:13). I am asking for your peace to rule and reign in my heart (Col. 3:15; Phil. 4:7) and that I would extend Your kingdom today through my thoughts, attitudes, words, and actions.

Please help me to be disciplined and get all Your work done today. Help me by revealing to my heart what I need to do next and give me the desire and the power to get that specific assignment accomplished (Phil. 2:13). Please continue to water (Is. 55:10) the 5 most important root attitudes in my heart: Surrender (Rom. 12:1), Trust (Pr. 3:5-6), Humility (Js. 4:8), Faith (Heb. 6:11) and Thanksgiving (Eph. 3:17).

Holy Spirit thank You for revealing the Father's Heart of Love to me today! I depend on You to lead and guide me! Help me practice the Scriptures every day! Thank You for being my constant companion. I'm truly grateful You are with me every moment! Thank You! Almighty God above all else today I'm longing to "know You" better today (Phil.3:10; John17:3)! "As the deer pants for streams of water, so I long for You, O God!" (Ps.42:1)

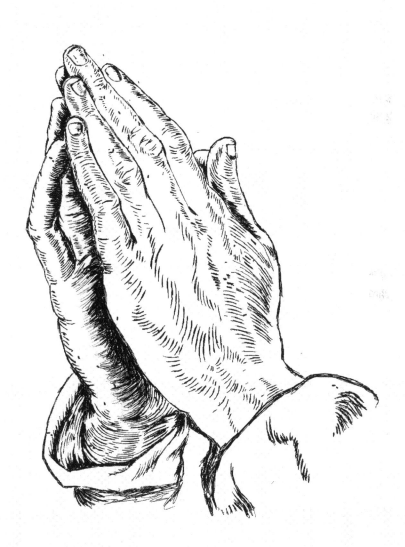

Scriptures to Pray

Over your mind...

Psalm 139:1-4
Proverbs 3:5-6
Psalm 139:23-24
Psalm 19:14
Proverbs 28:26
Romans 12:1-2
2 Corinthians 15:5
Ephesians 4:22-24
Philippians 4:6-8
Philippians 4:13
2 Timothy 1:7
Isaiah 26:3
Jeremiah 33:3
Mathew 21:22
Matthew 6:25
Colossians 3:2

Over your will...

Psalm 1:1-2
Psalm 16:7
Psalm 23:4
Psalm 23:6
Psalm 27:4-8
Psalm 30:1
Psalm 30:12
Psalm 31:7
Psalm 34:1
Psalm 39:1
Psalm 56:3-4
Psalm 57:2
Psalm 61:4
Psalm 63:4
Psalm 75:11
Psalm 75:12

Over your identity...

2 Corinthians 5:17
Colossians 2:10
Colossians 3:9-10
Ephesians 1:17-18
Ephesians 2:5
Romans 5:17
Romans 8:2
Isaiah 54:14
1 John 4:4
1 John 5:18
Ephesians 1:4
Ephesians 3:14-19
1 Peter 1:16
Philippians 4:7
Romans 8:15
John 15:9

Over your future...

Jeremiah 29:11
Philippians 3:20
Zephaniah 3:17
Romans 15:13
Isaiah 40:31
Psalm 39:7
Titus 2:11-15
Romans 12:9-21
2 Corinthians 4:17
Romans 8:18
Psalm 25:5
Psalm 31:14-15
Psalm 37:7

Over your past...

1 John 1:9
Phil. 3:13-14
Isaiah 43:18-19
Galatians 2:20-22
Mathew 6:15
Acts 2:38
Romans 2:7
Romans 8:1
2 Corinthians 5:17-18
Luke 9:62
Psalm 37: 1-6
Ephesians 1:4-5
Ephesians 1:7-9

Over God's will...

Hebrews 13:5
Isaiah 41:10
Zephaniah 3:17
Psalm 23
Isaiah 40:29
Isaiah 40:30
Isaiah 40:31
Isaiah 41:13
Isaiah 43:2
Isaiah 54:10
Isaiah 54:17
Isaiah 58:6
2 Chronicles 7:14

Scriptures to Pray

Leaders & Government...

I Timothy 2:1-2
I Peter 2:17
Romans 13:1
Jeremiah 29:7
2 Chronicles 7:14
Psalm 2:10-11
Psalm 46:1-11
Proverbs 11:14
Proverbs 21:1
Job 12:23-25
Isaiah 54:17
Isaiah 42:1-4
Psalm 4:8

Over your marraige...

Mark 11:24-25
Ephesians 4:32
Mathew 7:7-8
Psalm 127:1
Proverbs 24:3-4
Galatians 6:9
Proverbs 22:29
Proverbs 23:4-5
Mathew 16:26
Ecl. 10:18
Psalm 90:17
Ecclesiastes 5:19
Philippians 4:19

Over children...

Mathew 7:11
Psalm 103:17-18
1 John 4:9-11
Isaiah 65:23
Psalm 127:3
1 John 3:19-22
Psalm 91:1-2
Isaiah 43:2
Isaiah 54:17
2 Thess. 2:13
1 John 4:16
Proverbs 20:7
Psalm 139

Over protection...

2 Thess. 3:3
Psalm 91:1-0
Psalm 91:11-16
Psalm 138:7
John 17:15
Mark 11:24
Psalm 32:7
James 4:7
Hebrews 11:1
Psalm 121:1-8
Psalm 69:32
Psalm 69:33
Psalm 69:35
Psalm 69:36
1 Peter 3:12-141

Over provision...

Ephesians 3:20
2 Corinthians 9:8
2 Peter 1:3
Hebrews 13:5
John 10:10
1 Timothy 5:8
Luke 12:22-26
Luke 12:27-31
Luke 12:32-34
Matthew 6:33
Psalm 34:8
Psalm 37:4-6
Psalm 84:11
Psalm 135:3
Psalm 145:9

Over healing...

Psalm 30:2
Deu.31:6
Psalm 103:3
Psalm 86:7
Psalm 107:20
Psalm 139:23-24
Psalm 118:17
Proverbs 15:15
Psalm 147:3
1 Peter 5:7
Pro. 4:20-22
Isaiah 58:8
Jeremiah 17:14
1 Peter 2:24
3 John 2:2

Emerge Victorious

You are clothed with my purposes.
You are dressed with my plans.
You have now the mantel of praise.
I have chosen you.
I have separated you for myself.
You wear a crown of joy and kindness.
Remember I am your shepherd, The Good Shepherd.
I will lead you safely to green pastures of peace,
to still waters flowing with fresh water.

I sit with you. Remember, you are equipped with a powerful tool. You have the power to say a faith-filled 'NO!' to the enemy and to your own flesh. You can say 'NO!' to thoughts that pull you away from me. You can simply walk away from those thoughts. No need to mull them over, or worry about them, or live in fear of them. The freedom you've experienced was and is real. Live there. The address is John 3:16 and the crossroads are trust, hope & faith.

About your mind, don't worry but keep doing good, pray over your mind, meditate on my word, mull over my remarks, live them out diligently. Quickly do your best. I will reward you for your effort. The chains of fear are broken. The chains of anxiety are broken. The chains of toxic thoughts are broken. The power of the blood flowed over those thoughts, over those fears, over those labels, and it's power severed and broke their strongholds. You are free!

Emerge victorious!

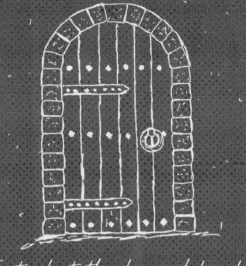

I stand at the door and knock.

"*Look! I stand at the door and knock. If you hear my voice and open the door, I will come in, and we will share a meal together as friends.*"

Revelation 3:20 (nlt)

Monthly Prayer Goals!

Look! I stand at the door and knock. If you hear my voice and open the door, I will come in, and we will share a meal together as friends.
Revelation 3:20 (nlt)

Memory verse:

....
....
....
....
....

Key words for this month:

....
....
....
....

Lies, shame or guilt you may be embracing and the truth to replace it:

....
....
....
....

Gauge your prayer life this month

We all have the tendency to forget to pray over certain areas of our lives. Use this gauge to help you identify areas that need a little bit more of your attention this month.
Head over to the 'scriptures to pray' section and choose a few scriptures to pray & declare.

GOVERNMENT

1 2 3 4 5 6 7 8 9 10

FAMILY

1 2 3 4 5 6 7 8 9 10

CHURCH

1 2 3 4 5 6 7 8 9 10

LIFE

1 2 3 4 5 6 7 8 9 10

THE LOST

1 2 3 4 5 6 7 8 9 10

MY NEEDS

1 2 3 4 5 6 7 8 9 10

Hopes & Dreams

DREAM WITH GOD IN MIND AND MAKE MARGIN FOR MIRACLES.

Government

I URGE, THEN, FIRST OF ALL,
THAT **PETITIONS, PRAYERS, INTERCESSION** AND **THANKSGIVING** BE MADE
FOR ALL PEOPLE—FOR KINGS AND ALL THOSE IN AUTHORITY, THAT WE MAY
LIVE PEACEFUL AND QUIET LIVES IN ALL GODLINESS AND HOLINESS. THIS IS
GOOD, AND PLEASES GOD OUR SAVIOR.
1 TIMOTHY 2:1-3 (NIV)

WHAT TO PRAY FOR:

WISE COUNSEL . TRUST IN GOD. PROTECTION . HOLY SPIRIT
GUIDANCE . COURAGE TO DO RIGHT . COMPASSIONATE
HEARTS . STRENGTH . DO GOD'S WILL . SALVATION

WHO TO PRAY FOR:

President

Governor

Mayor

Police Chief

Sheriff

City Leaders

Adopt-A-Cop

Here are six ways to pray for officers: pray they come to know Jesus Christ as their Savior. Pray for compassion in their hearts for the people they serve. Pray they would exhibit integrity, honesty and dedication. Pray for wisdom and understanding. Pray for their mental, emotional and physical health. Pray for their families.

Family

BEAR WITH EACH OTHER AND FORGIVE ONE ANOTHER IF ANY OF YOU
HAS A GRIEVANCE AGAINST SOMEONE. FORGIVE AS THE LORD
FORGAVE YOU. AND OVER ALL THESE VIRTUES PUT ON LOVE, WHICH
BINDS THEM ALL TOGETHER IN PERFECT UNITY.
COLOSSIANS 3:13-14 (NIV)

SPOUSE

CHILDREN

PARENTS/SIBLINGS

EXTENDED FAMILY

Church

YOU ALSO, AS LIVING STONES, ARE BEING BUILT UP AS A SPIRITUAL
HOUSE FOR A HOLY PRIESTHOOD, TO OFFER UP SPIRITUAL
SACRIFICES ACCEPTABLE TO GOD THROUGH JESUS CHRIST.
1 PETER 2:5 (NASB)

PASTOR(S)

LEADERSHIP

SMALL GROUP

MISSIONS

Life

I HAVE BEEN CRUCIFIED WITH CHRIST; IT IS NO LONGER I WHO LIVE,
BUT CHRIST LIVES IN ME; AND THE LIFE WHICH I NOW LIVE IN THE
FLESH I LIVE BY FAITH IN THE SON OF GOD, WHO LOVED ME AND
GAVE HIMSELF FOR ME.
GALATIANS 2:20 (NKJV)

EMPLOYER

EMPLOYEES/CO-WORKERS

MENTORS/TEACHERS

CLOSE FRIENDS

NEW FRIENDS

TEAMS I LEAD

The Lost

TO OPEN THEIR EYES, SO THAT THEY MAY TURN FROM DARKNESS TO LIGHT AND FROM THE POWER OF SATAN TO GOD, THAT THEY MAY RECEIVE FORGIVENESS OF SINS AND A PLACE AMONG THOSE WHO ARE SANCTIFIED BY FAITH IN ME.
ACTS 26:18 (NKJV)

FRIENDS. NEIGHBORS. CO-WORKERS. PEOPLE YOU MEET. FAMILY.

....

A Prayer for those who need to know Jesus.

Father,

I pray that you would draw my friends to Jesus today (John 6:44). Please bind the spirit that blinds their minds so that they may see the light of the gospel (2 Corinthians 4:4). I ask that the spirit of adoption would come upon them and that they would find freedom from fear and slavery to sin. I pray that your love would flood their minds and hearts. I ask that your love would cause them to cry out "Abba, Father," to you oh Lord! Father, I pray that they would experience an identity exchange from orphans to children of God today (Romans 3:15)! I ask that you would commission and orchestrate divine appointments with other Christians! You are the Lord of the Harvest and your word says that we are to ask you to send out workers. I come into agreement with your word right now (Matthew 9:38). Father, only you can give the Spirit of wisdom and of revelation in the knowledge of Jesus! I pray that you would release this amazing gift on their minds and hearts (Ephesians 1:17).

Finally Father, I pray that they would come to know what the length, and width, and height, and depth of Your amazing love! (Ephesians 3:18)

In Jesus name, Amen!

My Needs

BE ANXIOUS FOR NOTHING, BUT IN EVERYTHING BY PRAYER AND
SUPPLICATION, WITH THANKSGIVING, LET YOUR REQUESTS BE MADE
KNOWN TO GOD; AND THE PEACE OF GOD, WHICH SURPASSES ALL
UNDERSTANDING, WILL GUARD YOUR HEARTS AND MINDS THROUGH
CHRIST JESUS.
PHILIPPIANS 4:6-8 (NKJV)

PHYSICAL

RELATIONAL

FINANCIAL

SPIRITUAL

MENTAL/EMOTIONAL

MORE

Prayer Request

AND THIS IS THE CONFIDENCE THAT WE HAVE TOWARD HIM, THAT IF WE ASK
ANYTHING ACCORDING TO HIS WILL HE HEARS US. AND IF WE KNOW THAT HE
HEARS US IN WHATEVER WE ASK, WE KNOW THAT WE HAVE THE REQUESTS
THAT WE HAVE ASKED OF HIM.
1 JOHN 5:14-15 (ESV)

Prayer Request

FOR THE LORD GOD IS A SUN AND SHIELD: THE LORD WILL GIVE
GRACE AND GLORY: NO GOOD THING WILL HE WITHHOLD FROM THEM
THAT WALK UPRIGHTLY.
PSALM 84:11 (KJV)

DATE REQUESTED   DATE ANSWERED

Thank You!

NOW THANKS BE TO GOD WHO ALWAYS LEADS US IN TRIUMPH IN CHRIST, AND
THROUGH US DIFFUSES THE FRAGRANCE OF HIS KNOWLEDGE IN EVERY
PLACE. 2 CORINTHIANS 2:14 (NKJV)

1 ....
2 ....
3 ....
4 ....
5 ....
6 ....
7 ....
8 ....
9 ....
10 ....
11 ....
12 ....
13 ....
14 ....
15 ....
16 ....
17 ....
18 ....
19 ....
20 ....
21 ....
22 ....
23 ....
24 ....
25 ....
26 ....
27 ....
28 ....
29 ....
30 ....
31 ....

He waits for me to wake up
so we can start the day together.

"As for me, I shall behold your face in righteousness; when I awake, I shall be satisfied with your likeness."

Psalm 17:15 (esv)

Monthly Prayer Goals!

As for me, I shall behold your face in righteousness;
when I awake, I shall be satisfied with your likeness.
Psalm 17:15 (esv)

Memory verse:

....
....
....
....
....

Key words for this month:

....
....
....
....

Lies, shame or guilt you may be embracing and the truth to replace it:

....
....
....
....

Gauge your prayer life this month

We all have the tendency to forget to pray over certain areas
of our lives. Use this gauge to help you identify areas that
need a little bit more of your attention this month.
Head over to the 'scriptures to pray' section and choose a few
scriptures to pray & declare.

GOVERNMENT

1 2 3 4 5 6 7 8 9 10

FAMILY

1 2 3 4 5 6 7 8 9 10

CHURCH

1 2 3 4 5 6 7 8 9 10

LIFE

1 2 3 4 5 6 7 8 9 10

THE LOST

1 2 3 4 5 6 7 8 9 10

MY NEEDS

1 2 3 4 5 6 7 8 9 10

Hopes & Dreams

DREAM WITH GOD IN MIND AND MAKE MARGIN FOR MIRACLES.

Government

I URGE, THEN, FIRST OF ALL,
THAT **PETITIONS, PRAYERS, INTERCESSION** AND **THANKSGIVING** BE MADE
FOR ALL PEOPLE—FOR KINGS AND ALL THOSE IN AUTHORITY, THAT WE MAY
LIVE PEACEFUL AND QUIET LIVES IN ALL GODLINESS AND HOLINESS. THIS IS
GOOD, AND PLEASES GOD OUR SAVIOR.
1 TIMOTHY 2:1-3 (NIV)

WHAT TO PRAY FOR:

WISE COUNSEL . TRUST IN GOD. PROTECTION . HOLY SPIRIT
GUIDANCE . COURAGE TO DO RIGHT . COMPASSIONATE
HEARTS . STRENGTH . DO GOD'S WILL . SALVATION

WHO TO PRAY FOR:

....
President

....
Governor

....
Mayor

....
Police Chief

....
Sheriff

....
City Leaders

....
Adopt-A-Cop

Here are six ways to pray for officers: pray they come to know Jesus Christ as their Savior. Pray
for compassion in their hearts for the people they serve. Pray they would exhibit integrity,
honesty and dedication. Pray for wisdom and understanding. Pray for their mental, emotional
and physical health. Pray for their families.

Family

BEAR WITH EACH OTHER AND FORGIVE ONE ANOTHER IF ANY OF YOU
HAS A GRIEVANCE AGAINST SOMEONE. FORGIVE AS THE LORD
FORGAVE YOU. AND OVER ALL THESE VIRTUES PUT ON LOVE, WHICH
BINDS THEM ALL TOGETHER IN PERFECT UNITY.
COLOSSIANS 3:13-14 (NIV)

SPOUSE

CHILDREN

PARENTS/SIBLINGS

EXTENDED FAMILY

Church

YOU ALSO, AS LIVING STONES, ARE BEING BUILT UP AS A SPIRITUAL
HOUSE FOR A HOLY PRIESTHOOD, TO OFFER UP SPIRITUAL
SACRIFICES ACCEPTABLE TO GOD THROUGH JESUS CHRIST.
1 PETER 2:5 (NASB)

PASTOR(S)

LEADERSHIP

SMALL GROUP

MISSIONS

Life

I HAVE BEEN CRUCIFIED WITH CHRIST; IT IS NO LONGER I WHO LIVE,
BUT CHRIST LIVES IN ME; AND THE LIFE WHICH I NOW LIVE IN THE
FLESH I LIVE BY FAITH IN THE SON OF GOD, WHO LOVED ME AND
GAVE HIMSELF FOR ME.
GALATIANS 2:20 (NKJV)

EMPLOYER

EMPLOYEES/CO-WORKERS

MENTORS/TEACHERS

CLOSE FRIENDS

NEW FRIENDS

TEAMS I LEAD

The Lost

TO OPEN THEIR EYES, SO THAT THEY MAY TURN FROM DARKNESS TO LIGHT AND FROM THE POWER OF SATAN TO GOD, THAT THEY MAY RECEIVE FORGIVENESS OF SINS AND A PLACE AMONG THOSE WHO ARE SANCTIFIED BY FAITH IN ME.
ACTS 26:18 (NKJV)

FRIENDS. NEIGHBORS. CO-WORKERS. PEOPLE YOU MEET. FAMILY.

....

A Prayer for those who need to know Jesus...

Father,

I pray that you would draw my friends to Jesus today (John 6:44). Please bind the spirit that blinds their minds so that they may see the light of the gospel (2 Corinthians 4:4). I ask that the spirit of adoption would come upon them and that they would find freedom from fear and slavery to sin. I pray that your love would flood their minds and hearts. I ask that your love would cause them to cry out "Abba, Father," to you oh Lord! Father, I pray that they would experience an identity exchange from orphans to children of God today (Romans 3:15)! I ask that you would commission and orchestrate divine appointments with other Christians! You are the Lord of the Harvest and your word says that we are to ask you to send out workers. I come into agreement with your word right now (Matthew 9:38). Father, only you can give the Spirit of wisdom and of revelation in the knowledge of Jesus! I pray that you would release this amazing gift on their minds and hearts (Ephesians 1:17).

Finally Father, I pray that they would come to know what the length, and width, and height, and depth of Your amazing love! (Ephesians 3:18)

In Jesus name, Amen!

My Needs

BE ANXIOUS FOR NOTHING, BUT IN EVERYTHING BY PRAYER AND
SUPPLICATION, WITH THANKSGIVING, LET YOUR REQUESTS BE MADE
KNOWN TO GOD; AND THE PEACE OF GOD, WHICH SURPASSES ALL
UNDERSTANDING, WILL GUARD YOUR HEARTS AND MINDS THROUGH
CHRIST JESUS.
PHILIPPIANS 4:6-8 (NKJV)

PHYSICAL

RELATIONAL

FINANCIAL

SPIRITUAL

MENTAL/EMOTIONAL

MORE

Prayer Request

AND THIS IS THE CONFIDENCE THAT WE HAVE TOWARD HIM, THAT IF WE ASK
ANYTHING ACCORDING TO HIS WILL HE HEARS US. AND IF WE KNOW THAT HE
HEARS US IN WHATEVER WE ASK, WE KNOW THAT WE HAVE THE REQUESTS
THAT WE HAVE ASKED OF HIM.
1 JOHN 5:14-15 (ESV)

Prayer Request

FOR THE LORD GOD IS A SUN AND SHIELD: THE LORD WILL GIVE
GRACE AND GLORY: NO GOOD THING WILL HE WITHHOLD FROM THEM
THAT WALK UPRIGHTLY.
PSALM 84:11 (KJV)

DATE REQUESTED

DATE ANSWERED

Thank You!

NOW THANKS BE TO GOD WHO ALWAYS LEADS US IN TRIUMPH IN CHRIST, AND
THROUGH US DIFFUSES THE FRAGRANCE OF HIS KNOWLEDGE IN EVERY
PLACE. 2 CORINTHIANS 2:14 (NKJV)

1 ....
2 ....
3 ....
4 ....
5 ....
6 ....
7 ....
8 ....
9 ....
10 ....
11 ....
12 ....
13 ....
14 ....
15 ....
16 ....
17 ....
18 ....
19 ....
20 ....
21 ....
22 ....
23 ....
24 ....
25 ....
26 ....
27 ....
28 ....
29 ....
30 ....
31 ....

You are not alone in this fire.

"But now, O Jacob, listen to the LORD who created you. O Israel, the one who formed you says, "Do not be afraid, for I have ransomed you. I have called you by name; you are mine. When you go through deep waters, I will be with you. When you go through rivers of difficulty, you will not drown. When you walk through the fire of oppression, you will not be burned up; the flames will not consume you."

Isaiah 43:1-2 (nlt)

Monthly Prayer Goals!

When you go through deep waters, I will be with you. When you go through rivers of difficulty, you will not drown. When you walk through the fire of oppression, you will not be burned up; the flames will not consume you.
Isaiah 43:1-2 (Nlt)

Memory verse:

....
....
....
....
....

Key words for this month:

....
....
....
....

Lies, shame or guilt you may be embracing and the truth to replace it:

....
....
....
....

Gauge your prayer life this month

We all have the tendency to forget to pray over certain areas of our lives. Use this gauge to help you identify areas that need a little bit more of your attention this month.
Head over to the 'scriptures to pray' section and choose a few scriptures to pray & declare.

GOVERNMENT

1 2 3 4 5 6 7 8 9 10

LIFE

1 2 3 4 5 6 7 8 9 10

FAMILY

1 2 3 4 5 6 7 8 9 10

THE LOST

1 2 3 4 5 6 7 8 9 10

CHURCH

1 2 3 4 5 6 7 8 9 10

MY NEEDS

1 2 3 4 5 6 7 8 9 10

Hopes & Dreams

DREAM WITH GOD IN MIND AND MAKE MARGIN FOR MIRACLES.

Government

I URGE, THEN, FIRST OF ALL,
THAT **PETITIONS, PRAYERS, INTERCESSION** AND **THANKSGIVING** BE MADE
FOR ALL PEOPLE—FOR KINGS AND ALL THOSE IN AUTHORITY, THAT WE MAY
LIVE PEACEFUL AND QUIET LIVES IN ALL GODLINESS AND HOLINESS. THIS IS
GOOD, AND PLEASES GOD OUR SAVIOR.
1 TIMOTHY 2:1-3 (NIV)

WHAT TO PRAY FOR:

WISE COUNSEL . TRUST IN GOD. PROTECTION . HOLY SPIRIT
GUIDANCE . COURAGE TO DO RIGHT . COMPASSIONATE
HEARTS . STRENGTH . DO GOD'S WILL . SALVATION

WHO TO PRAY FOR:

....
President

....
Governor

....
Mayor

....
Police Chief

....
Sheriff

....
City Leaders

....
Adopt-A-Cop

Here are six ways to pray for officers: pray they come to know Jesus Christ as their Savior. Pray
for compassion in their hearts for the people they serve. Pray they would exhibit integrity,
honesty and dedication. Pray for wisdom and understanding. Pray for their mental, emotional
and physical health. Pray for their families.

Family

BEAR WITH EACH OTHER AND FORGIVE ONE ANOTHER IF ANY OF YOU
HAS A GRIEVANCE AGAINST SOMEONE. FORGIVE AS THE LORD
FORGAVE YOU. AND OVER ALL THESE VIRTUES PUT ON LOVE, WHICH
BINDS THEM ALL TOGETHER IN PERFECT UNITY.
COLOSSIANS 3:13-14 (NIV)

SPOUSE

CHILDREN

PARENTS/SIBLINGS

EXTENDED FAMILY

Church

YOU ALSO, AS LIVING STONES, ARE BEING BUILT UP AS A SPIRITUAL
HOUSE FOR A HOLY PRIESTHOOD, TO OFFER UP SPIRITUAL
SACRIFICES ACCEPTABLE TO GOD THROUGH JESUS CHRIST.
1 PETER 2:5 (NASB)

PASTOR(S)

LEADERSHIP

SMALL GROUP

MISSIONS

Life

I HAVE BEEN CRUCIFIED WITH CHRIST; IT IS NO LONGER I WHO LIVE,
BUT CHRIST LIVES IN ME; AND THE LIFE WHICH I NOW LIVE IN THE
FLESH I LIVE BY FAITH IN THE SON OF GOD, WHO LOVED ME AND
GAVE HIMSELF FOR ME.
GALATIANS 2:20 (NKJV)

EMPLOYER

EMPLOYEES/CO-WORKERS

MENTORS/TEACHERS

CLOSE FRIENDS

NEW FRIENDS

TEAMS I LEAD

The Lost

TO OPEN THEIR EYES, SO THAT THEY MAY TURN FROM DARKNESS TO LIGHT AND FROM THE POWER OF SATAN TO GOD, THAT THEY MAY RECEIVE FORGIVENESS OF SINS AND A PLACE AMONG THOSE WHO ARE SANCTIFIED BY FAITH IN ME.
ACTS 26:18 (NKJV)

FRIENDS. NEIGHBORS. CO-WORKERS. PEOPLE YOU MEET. FAMILY.

. . . .

A Prayer for those who need to know Jesus.

Father,

I pray that you would draw my friends to Jesus today (John 6:44). Please bind the spirit that blinds their minds so that they may see the light of the gospel (2 Corinthians 4:4). I ask that the spirit of adoption would come upon them and that they would find freedom from fear and slavery to sin. I pray that your love would flood their minds and hearts. I ask that your love would cause them to cry out "Abba, Father," to you oh Lord! Father, I pray that they would experience an identity exchange from orphans to children of God today (Romans 3:15)! I ask that you would commission and orchestrate divine appointments with other Christians! You are the Lord of the Harvest and your word says that we are to ask you to send out workers. I come into agreement with your word right now (Matthew 9:38). Father, only you can give the Spirit of wisdom and of revelation in the knowledge of Jesus! I pray that you would release this amazing gift on their minds and hearts (Ephesians 1:17).

Finally Father, I pray that they would come to know what the length, and width, and height, and depth of Your amazing love! (Ephesians 3:18)

In Jesus name, Amen!

My Needs

BE ANXIOUS FOR NOTHING, BUT IN EVERYTHING BY PRAYER AND
SUPPLICATION, WITH THANKSGIVING, LET YOUR REQUESTS BE MADE
KNOWN TO GOD; AND THE PEACE OF GOD, WHICH SURPASSES ALL
UNDERSTANDING, WILL GUARD YOUR HEARTS AND MINDS THROUGH
CHRIST JESUS.
PHILIPPIANS 4:6-8 (NKJV)

PHYSICAL

RELATIONAL

FINANCIAL

SPIRITUAL

MENTAL/EMOTIONAL

MORE

Prayer Request

AND THIS IS THE CONFIDENCE THAT WE HAVE TOWARD HIM, THAT IF WE ASK ANYTHING ACCORDING TO HIS WILL HE HEARS US. AND IF WE KNOW THAT HE HEARS US IN WHATEVER WE ASK, WE KNOW THAT WE HAVE THE REQUESTS THAT WE HAVE ASKED OF HIM.

1 JOHN 5:14-15 (ESV)

Prayer Request

FOR THE LORD GOD IS A SUN AND SHIELD: THE LORD WILL GIVE
GRACE AND GLORY: NO GOOD THING WILL HE WITHHOLD FROM THEM
THAT WALK UPRIGHTLY.
PSALM 84:11 (KJV)

DATE REQUESTED	DATE ANSWERED

Thank You!

NOW THANKS BE TO GOD WHO ALWAYS LEADS US IN TRIUMPH IN CHRIST, AND
THROUGH US DIFFUSES THE FRAGRANCE OF HIS KNOWLEDGE IN EVERY
PLACE. 2 CORINTHIANS 2:14 (NKJV)

1 ....
2 ....
3 ....
4 ....
5 ....
6 ....
7 ....
8 ....
9 ....
10 ....
11 ....
12 ....
13 ....
14 ....
15 ....
16 ....
17 ....
18 ....
19 ....
20 ....
21 ....
22 ....
23 ....
24 ....
25 ....
26 ....
27 ....
28 ....
29 ....
30 ....
31 ....

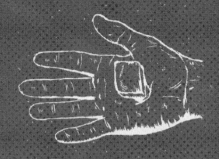

I have engraved you in the palm of my hands...

"Behold, I have engraved you on the palms of my hands; your walls are continually before me."

Isaiah 49:16 (esv)

Monthly Prayer Goals!

Behold, I have engraved you on the palms of my hands;
your walls are continually before me.
Isaiah 49:16 (esv)

Memory verse:

....
....
....
....
....

Key words for this month:

....
....
....
....

Lies, shame or guilt you may be embracing and the truth to replace it:

....
....
....
....

Gauge your prayer life this month

We all have the tendency to forget to pray over certain areas
of our lives. Use this gauge to help you identify areas that
need a little bit more of your attention this month.
Head over to the 'scriptures to pray' section and choose a few
scriptures to pray & declare.

GOVERNMENT   LIFE

1 2 3 4 5 6 7 8 9 10   1 2 3 4 5 6 7 8 9 10

FAMILY   THE LOST

1 2 3 4 5 6 7 8 9 10   1 2 3 4 5 6 7 8 9 10

CHURCH   MY NEEDS

1 2 3 4 5 6 7 8 9 10   1 2 3 4 5 6 7 8 9 10

Hopes & Dreams

DREAM WITH GOD IN MIND AND MAKE MARGIN FOR MIRACLES.

Government

I URGE, THEN, FIRST OF ALL,
THAT **PETITIONS, PRAYERS, INTERCESSION** AND **THANKSGIVING** BE MADE
FOR ALL PEOPLE—FOR KINGS AND ALL THOSE IN AUTHORITY, THAT WE MAY
LIVE PEACEFUL AND QUIET LIVES IN ALL GODLINESS AND HOLINESS. THIS IS
GOOD, AND PLEASES GOD OUR SAVIOR.
1 TIMOTHY 2:1-3 (NIV)

WHAT TO PRAY FOR:

WISE COUNSEL . TRUST IN GOD. PROTECTION . HOLY SPIRIT
GUIDANCE . COURAGE TO DO RIGHT . COMPASSIONATE
HEARTS . STRENGTH . DO GOD'S WILL . SALVATION

WHO TO PRAY FOR:

....
President

....
Governor

....
Mayor

....
Police Chief

....
Sheriff

....
City Leaders

....
Adopt-A-Cop

Here are six ways to pray for officers: pray they come to know Jesus Christ as their Savior. Pray
for compassion in their hearts for the people they serve. Pray they would exhibit integrity,
honesty and dedication. Pray for wisdom and understanding. Pray for their mental, emotional
and physical health. Pray for their families.

Family

BEAR WITH EACH OTHER AND FORGIVE ONE ANOTHER IF ANY OF YOU
HAS A GRIEVANCE AGAINST SOMEONE. FORGIVE AS THE LORD
FORGAVE YOU. AND OVER ALL THESE VIRTUES PUT ON LOVE, WHICH
BINDS THEM ALL TOGETHER IN PERFECT UNITY.
COLOSSIANS 3:13-14 (NIV)

SPOUSE

CHILDREN

PARENTS/SIBLINGS

EXTENDED FAMILY

Church

YOU ALSO, AS LIVING STONES, ARE BEING BUILT UP AS A SPIRITUAL
HOUSE FOR A HOLY PRIESTHOOD, TO OFFER UP SPIRITUAL
SACRIFICES ACCEPTABLE TO GOD THROUGH JESUS CHRIST.
1 PETER 2:5 (NASB)

PASTOR(S)

LEADERSHIP

SMALL GROUP

MISSIONS

Life

I HAVE BEEN CRUCIFIED WITH CHRIST; IT IS NO LONGER I WHO LIVE,
BUT CHRIST LIVES IN ME; AND THE LIFE WHICH I NOW LIVE IN THE
FLESH I LIVE BY FAITH IN THE SON OF GOD, WHO LOVED ME AND
GAVE HIMSELF FOR ME.
GALATIANS 2:20 (NKJV)

EMPLOYER

EMPLOYEES/CO-WORKERS

MENTORS/TEACHERS

CLOSE FRIENDS

NEW FRIENDS

TEAMS I LEAD

The Lost

TO OPEN THEIR EYES, SO THAT THEY MAY TURN FROM DARKNESS TO
LIGHT AND FROM THE POWER OF SATAN TO GOD, THAT THEY MAY
RECEIVE FORGIVENESS OF SINS AND A PLACE AMONG THOSE WHO
ARE SANCTIFIED BY FAITH IN ME.
ACTS 26:18 (NKJV)

FRIENDS. NEIGHBORS. CO-WORKERS. PEOPLE YOU MEET. FAMILY.

....

A Prayer for those who need to know Jesus...

Father,

I pray that you would draw my friends to Jesus today
(John 6:44). Please bind the spirit that blinds their minds so
that they may see the light of the gospel (2 Corinthians 4:4). I
ask that the spirit of adoption would come upon them and that
they would find freedom from fear and slavery to sin. I pray
that your love would flood their minds and hearts. I ask that
your love would cause them to cry out "Abba, Father," to you
oh Lord! Father, I pray that they would experience an identity
exchange from orphans to children of God today (Romans
3:15)! I ask that you would commission and orchestrate divine
appointments with other Christians! You are the Lord of the
Harvest and your word says that we are to ask you to send out
workers. I come into agreement with your word right now
(Matthew 9:38). Father, only you can give the Spirit of wisdom
and of revelation in the knowledge of Jesus! I pray that you
would release this amazing gift on their minds and hearts
(Ephesians 1:17).

Finally Father, I pray that they would come to know what the
length, and width, and height, and depth of Your amazing
love! (Ephesians 3:18)

In Jesus name, Amen!

My Needs

BE ANXIOUS FOR NOTHING, BUT IN EVERYTHING BY PRAYER AND
SUPPLICATION, WITH THANKSGIVING, LET YOUR REQUESTS BE MADE
KNOWN TO GOD; AND THE PEACE OF GOD, WHICH SURPASSES ALL
UNDERSTANDING, WILL GUARD YOUR HEARTS AND MINDS THROUGH
CHRIST JESUS.
PHILIPPIANS 4:6-8 (NKJV)

PHYSICAL

RELATIONAL

FINANCIAL

SPIRITUAL

MENTAL/EMOTIONAL

MORE

Prayer Request

AND THIS IS THE CONFIDENCE THAT WE HAVE TOWARD HIM, THAT IF WE ASK ANYTHING ACCORDING TO HIS WILL HE HEARS US. AND IF WE KNOW THAT HE HEARS US IN WHATEVER WE ASK, WE KNOW THAT WE HAVE THE REQUESTS THAT WE HAVE ASKED OF HIM.
1 JOHN 5:14-15 (ESV)

Prayer Request

FOR THE LORD GOD IS A SUN AND SHIELD: THE LORD WILL GIVE
GRACE AND GLORY: NO GOOD THING WILL HE WITHHOLD FROM THEM
THAT WALK UPRIGHTLY.
PSALM 84:11 (KJV)

DATE REQUESTED	DATE ANSWERED

Thank You!

NOW THANKS BE TO GOD WHO ALWAYS LEADS US IN TRIUMPH IN CHRIST, AND
THROUGH US DIFFUSES THE FRAGRANCE OF HIS KNOWLEDGE IN EVERY
PLACE. 2 CORINTHIANS 2:14 (NKJV)

1 ....
2 ....
3 ....
4 ....
5 ....
6 ....
7 ....
8 ....
9 ....
10 ....
11 ....
12 ....
13 ....
14 ....
15 ....
16 ....
17 ....
18 ....
19 ....
20 ....
21 ....
22 ....
23 ....
24 ....
25 ....
26 ....
27 ....
28 ....
29 ....
30 ....
31 ....

*Only the one who paid the price
for you knows your value*

"*You were dead because of your sins and because your sinful nature was not yet cut away. Then God made you alive with Christ, for he forgave all our sins. He canceled the record of the charges against us and took it away by nailing it to the cross. In this way, he disarmed the spiritual rulers and authorities. He shamed them publicly by his victory over them on the cross.*"

Colossians 2:13-15 (nlt)

Monthly Prayer Goals!

He canceled the record of the charges against us and took it away by nailing it to the cross.
Colossians 2:14 (nlt)

Memory verse:

....
....
....
....
....

Key words for this month:

....
....
....
....

Lies, shame or guilt you may be embracing and the truth to replace it:

....
....
....
....

Gauge your prayer life this month

We all have the tendency to forget to pray over certain areas of our lives. Use this gauge to help you identify areas that need a little bit more of your attention this month.
Head over to the 'scriptures to pray' section and choose a few scriptures to pray & declare.

GOVERNMENT

1 2 3 4 5 6 7 8 9 10

FAMILY

1 2 3 4 5 6 7 8 9 10

CHURCH

1 2 3 4 5 6 7 8 9 10

LIFE

1 2 3 4 5 6 7 8 9 10

THE LOST

1 2 3 4 5 6 7 8 9 10

MY NEEDS

1 2 3 4 5 6 7 8 9 10

Hopes & Dreams

DREAM WITH GOD IN MIND AND MAKE MARGIN FOR MIRACLES.

Government

I URGE, THEN, FIRST OF ALL,
THAT **PETITIONS, PRAYERS, INTERCESSION** AND **THANKSGIVING** BE MADE
FOR ALL PEOPLE—FOR KINGS AND ALL THOSE IN AUTHORITY, THAT WE MAY
LIVE PEACEFUL AND QUIET LIVES IN ALL GODLINESS AND HOLINESS. THIS IS
GOOD, AND PLEASES GOD OUR SAVIOR.
1 TIMOTHY 2:1-3 (NIV)

WHAT TO PRAY FOR:

WISE COUNSEL . TRUST IN GOD. PROTECTION . HOLY SPIRIT
GUIDANCE . COURAGE TO DO RIGHT . COMPASSIONATE
HEARTS . STRENGTH . DO GOD'S WILL . SALVATION

WHO TO PRAY FOR:

....
President

....
Governor

....
Mayor

....
Police Chief

....
Sheriff

....
City Leaders

....
Adopt-A-Cop

Here are six ways to pray for officers: pray they come to know Jesus Christ as their Savior. Pray
for compassion in their hearts for the people they serve. Pray they would exhibit integrity,
honesty and dedication. Pray for wisdom and understanding. Pray for their mental, emotional
and physical health. Pray for their families.

Family

BEAR WITH EACH OTHER AND FORGIVE ONE ANOTHER IF ANY OF YOU HAS A GRIEVANCE AGAINST SOMEONE. FORGIVE AS THE LORD FORGAVE YOU. AND OVER ALL THESE VIRTUES PUT ON LOVE, WHICH BINDS THEM ALL TOGETHER IN PERFECT UNITY.
COLOSSIANS 3:13-14 (NIV)

SPOUSE

CHILDREN

PARENTS/SIBLINGS

EXTENDED FAMILY

Church

YOU ALSO, AS LIVING STONES, ARE BEING BUILT UP AS A SPIRITUAL
HOUSE FOR A HOLY PRIESTHOOD, TO OFFER UP SPIRITUAL
SACRIFICES ACCEPTABLE TO GOD THROUGH JESUS CHRIST.
1 PETER 2:5 (NASB)

PASTOR(S)

LEADERSHIP

SMALL GROUP

MISSIONS

Life

I HAVE BEEN CRUCIFIED WITH CHRIST; IT IS NO LONGER I WHO LIVE,
BUT CHRIST LIVES IN ME; AND THE LIFE WHICH I NOW LIVE IN THE
FLESH I LIVE BY FAITH IN THE SON OF GOD, WHO LOVED ME AND
GAVE HIMSELF FOR ME.
GALATIANS 2:20 (NKJV)

EMPLOYER

EMPLOYEES/CO-WORKERS

MENTORS/TEACHERS

CLOSE FRIENDS

NEW FRIENDS

TEAMS I LEAD

The Lost

TO OPEN THEIR EYES, SO THAT THEY MAY TURN FROM DARKNESS TO LIGHT AND FROM THE POWER OF SATAN TO GOD, THAT THEY MAY RECEIVE FORGIVENESS OF SINS AND A PLACE AMONG THOSE WHO ARE SANCTIFIED BY FAITH IN ME.
ACTS 26:18 (NKJV)

FRIENDS. NEIGHBORS. CO-WORKERS. PEOPLE YOU MEET. FAMILY.

A Prayer for those who need to know Jesus

Father,

I pray that you would draw my friends to Jesus today (John 6:44). Please bind the spirit that blinds their minds so that they may see the light of the gospel (2 Corinthians 4:4). I ask that the spirit of adoption would come upon them and that they would find freedom from fear and slavery to sin. I pray that your love would flood their minds and hearts. I ask that your love would cause them to cry out "Abba, Father," to you oh Lord! Father, I pray that they would experience an identity exchange from orphans to children of God today (Romans 3:15)! I ask that you would commission and orchestrate divine appointments with other Christians! You are the Lord of the Harvest and your word says that we are to ask you to send out workers. I come into agreement with your word right now (Matthew 9:38). Father, only you can give the Spirit of wisdom and of revelation in the knowledge of Jesus! I pray that you would release this amazing gift on their minds and hearts (Ephesians 1:17).

Finally Father, I pray that they would come to know what the length, and width, and height, and depth of Your amazing love! (Ephesians 3:18)

In Jesus name, Amen!

My Needs

BE ANXIOUS FOR NOTHING, BUT IN EVERYTHING BY PRAYER AND SUPPLICATION, WITH THANKSGIVING, LET YOUR REQUESTS BE MADE KNOWN TO GOD; AND THE PEACE OF GOD, WHICH SURPASSES ALL UNDERSTANDING, WILL GUARD YOUR HEARTS AND MINDS THROUGH CHRIST JESUS.
PHILIPPIANS 4:6-8 (NKJV)

PHYSICAL

RELATIONAL

FINANCIAL

SPIRITUAL

MENTAL/EMOTIONAL

MORE

Prayer Request

AND THIS IS THE CONFIDENCE THAT WE HAVE TOWARD HIM, THAT IF WE ASK
ANYTHING ACCORDING TO HIS WILL HE HEARS US. AND IF WE KNOW THAT HE
HEARS US IN WHATEVER WE ASK, WE KNOW THAT WE HAVE THE REQUESTS
THAT WE HAVE ASKED OF HIM.
1 JOHN 5:14-15 (ESV)

Prayer Request

FOR THE LORD GOD IS A SUN AND SHIELD: THE LORD WILL GIVE
GRACE AND GLORY: NO GOOD THING WILL HE WITHHOLD FROM THEM
THAT WALK UPRIGHTLY.
PSALM 84:11 (KJV)

DATE REQUESTED   DATE ANSWERED

Thank You!

NOW THANKS BE TO GOD WHO ALWAYS LEADS US IN TRIUMPH IN CHRIST, AND THROUGH US DIFFUSES THE FRAGRANCE OF HIS KNOWLEDGE IN EVERY PLACE. 2 CORINTHIANS 2:14 (NKJV)

1 ....
2 ....
3 ....
4 ....
5 ....
6 ....
7 ....
8 ....
9 ....
10 ....
11 ....
12 ....
13 ....
14 ....
15 ....
16 ....
17 ....
18 ....
19 ....
20 ....
21 ....
22 ....
23 ....
24 ....
25 ....
26 ....
27 ....
28 ....
29 ....
30 ....
31 ....

I was lost but now I'm found.

"Then Jesus told them this parable: "Suppose one of you has a hundred sheep and loses one of them. Doesn't he leave the ninety-nine in the open country and go after the lost sheep until he finds it? And when he finds it, he joyfully puts it on his shoulders and goes home. Then he calls his friends and neighbors together and says, 'Rejoice with me; I have found my lost sheep.' I tell you that in the same way there will be more rejoicing in heaven over one sinner who repents than over ninety-nine righteous persons who do not need to repent."

Luke 15:3-7 (niv)

Monthly Prayer Goals!

I tell you that in the same way there will be more rejoicing in heaven over one sinner who repents than over ninety-nine righteous persons who do not need to repent.
Luke 15:7 (niv)

Memory verse:

....
....
....
....
....

Key words for this month:

....
....
....
....

Lies, shame or guilt you may be embracing and the truth to replace it:

....
....
....
....

Gauge your prayer life this month

We all have the tendency to forget to pray over certain areas of our lives. Use this gauge to help you identify areas that need a little bit more of your attention this month.
Head over to the 'scriptures to pray' section and choose a few scriptures to pray & declare.

GOVERNMENT

1 2 3 4 5 6 7 8 9 10

FAMILY

1 2 3 4 5 6 7 8 9 10

CHURCH

1 2 3 4 5 6 7 8 9 10

LIFE

1 2 3 4 5 6 7 8 9 10

THE LOST

1 2 3 4 5 6 7 8 9 10

MY NEEDS

1 2 3 4 5 6 7 8 9 10

Hopes & Dreams

DREAM WITH GOD IN MIND AND MAKE MARGIN FOR MIRACLES.

Government

I URGE, THEN, FIRST OF ALL,
THAT **PETITIONS, PRAYERS, INTERCESSION** AND **THANKSGIVING** BE MADE
FOR ALL PEOPLE—FOR KINGS AND ALL THOSE IN AUTHORITY, THAT WE MAY
LIVE PEACEFUL AND QUIET LIVES IN ALL GODLINESS AND HOLINESS. THIS IS
GOOD, AND PLEASES GOD OUR SAVIOR.
1 TIMOTHY 2:1-3 (NIV)

WHAT TO PRAY FOR:

WISE COUNSEL . TRUST IN GOD. PROTECTION . HOLY SPIRIT
GUIDANCE . COURAGE TO DO RIGHT . COMPASSIONATE
HEARTS . STRENGTH . DO GOD'S WILL . SALVATION

WHO TO PRAY FOR:

....
President

....
Governor

....
Mayor

....
Police Chief

....
Sheriff

....
City Leaders

....
Adopt-A-Cop

Here are six ways to pray for officers: pray they come to know Jesus Christ as their Savior. Pray
for compassion in their hearts for the people they serve. Pray they would exhibit integrity,
honesty and dedication. Pray for wisdom and understanding. Pray for their mental, emotional
and physical health. Pray for their families.

Family

BEAR WITH EACH OTHER AND FORGIVE ONE ANOTHER IF ANY OF YOU
HAS A GRIEVANCE AGAINST SOMEONE. FORGIVE AS THE LORD
FORGAVE YOU. AND OVER ALL THESE VIRTUES PUT ON LOVE, WHICH
BINDS THEM ALL TOGETHER IN PERFECT UNITY.
COLOSSIANS 3:13-14 (NIV)

SPOUSE

CHILDREN

PARENTS/SIBLINGS

EXTENDED FAMILY

Church

YOU ALSO, AS LIVING STONES, ARE BEING BUILT UP AS A SPIRITUAL
HOUSE FOR A HOLY PRIESTHOOD, TO OFFER UP SPIRITUAL
SACRIFICES ACCEPTABLE TO GOD THROUGH JESUS CHRIST.
1 PETER 2:5 (NASB)

PASTOR(S)

LEADERSHIP

SMALL GROUP

MISSIONS

Life

I HAVE BEEN CRUCIFIED WITH CHRIST; IT IS NO LONGER I WHO LIVE,
BUT CHRIST LIVES IN ME; AND THE LIFE WHICH I NOW LIVE IN THE
FLESH I LIVE BY FAITH IN THE SON OF GOD, WHO LOVED ME AND
GAVE HIMSELF FOR ME.
GALATIANS 2:20 (NKJV)

EMPLOYER

EMPLOYEES/CO-WORKERS

MENTORS/TEACHERS

CLOSE FRIENDS

NEW FRIENDS

TEAMS I LEAD

The Lost

TO OPEN THEIR EYES, SO THAT THEY MAY TURN FROM DARKNESS TO
LIGHT AND FROM THE POWER OF SATAN TO GOD, THAT THEY MAY
RECEIVE FORGIVENESS OF SINS AND A PLACE AMONG THOSE WHO
ARE SANCTIFIED BY FAITH IN ME.
ACTS 26:18 (NKJV)

FRIENDS. NEIGHBORS. CO-WORKERS. PEOPLE YOU MEET. FAMILY.

A Prayer for those who need to know Jesus.

Father,

I pray that you would draw my friends to Jesus today
(John 6:44). Please bind the spirit that blinds their minds so
that they may see the light of the gospel (2 Corinthians 4:4). I
ask that the spirit of adoption would come upon them and that
they would find freedom from fear and slavery to sin. I pray
that your love would flood their minds and hearts. I ask that
your love would cause them to cry out "Abba, Father," to you
oh Lord! Father, I pray that they would experience an identity
exchange from orphans to children of God today (Romans
3:15)! I ask that you would commission and orchestrate divine
appointments with other Christians! You are the Lord of the
Harvest and your word says that we are to ask you to send out
workers. I come into agreement with your word right now
(Matthew 9:38). Father, only you can give the Spirit of wisdom
and of revelation in the knowledge of Jesus! I pray that you
would release this amazing gift on their minds and hearts
(Ephesians 1:17).

Finally Father, I pray that they would come to know what the
length, and width, and height, and depth of Your amazing
love! (Ephesians 3:18)

In Jesus' name. Amen!

My Needs

BE ANXIOUS FOR NOTHING, BUT IN EVERYTHING BY PRAYER AND SUPPLICATION, WITH THANKSGIVING, LET YOUR REQUESTS BE MADE KNOWN TO GOD; AND THE PEACE OF GOD, WHICH SURPASSES ALL UNDERSTANDING, WILL GUARD YOUR HEARTS AND MINDS THROUGH CHRIST JESUS.
PHILIPPIANS 4:6-8 (NKJV)

PHYSICAL

RELATIONAL

FINANCIAL

SPIRITUAL

MENTAL/EMOTIONAL

MORE

Prayer Request

AND THIS IS THE CONFIDENCE THAT WE HAVE TOWARD HIM, THAT IF WE ASK
ANYTHING ACCORDING TO HIS WILL HE HEARS US. AND IF WE KNOW THAT HE
HEARS US IN WHATEVER WE ASK, WE KNOW THAT WE HAVE THE REQUESTS
THAT WE HAVE ASKED OF HIM.
1 JOHN 5:14-15 (ESV)

Prayer Request

FOR THE LORD GOD IS A SUN AND SHIELD: THE LORD WILL GIVE
GRACE AND GLORY: NO GOOD THING WILL HE WITHHOLD FROM THEM
THAT WALK UPRIGHTLY.
PSALM 84:11 (KJV)

DATE REQUESTED   DATE ANSWERED

Thank You!

NOW THANKS BE TO GOD WHO ALWAYS LEADS US IN TRIUMPH IN CHRIST, AND THROUGH US DIFFUSES THE FRAGRANCE OF HIS KNOWLEDGE IN EVERY PLACE. 2 CORINTHIANS 2:14 (NKJV)

1 ....
2 ....
3 ....
4 ....
5 ....
6 ....
7 ....
8 ....
9 ....
10 ....
11 ....
12 ....
13 ....
14 ....
15 ....
16 ....
17 ....
18 ....
19 ....
20 ....
21 ....
22 ....
23 ....
24 ....
25 ....
26 ....
27 ....
28 ....
29 ....
30 ....
31 ....

You are my treasure

"*For you are a people holy to the Lord your God. The Lord your God has chosen you to be a people for his treasured possession, out of all the peoples who are on the face of the earth.*"

Deuteronomy 7:6 (esv)

Monthly Prayer Goals!

For you are a people holy to the Lord your God. The Lord your God has chosen you to be a people for his treasured possession, out of all the peoples who are on the face of the earth. Deuteronomy 7:6 (esv)

Memory verse:

....
....
....
....
....

Key words for this month:

....
....
....
....

Lies, shame or guilt you may be embracing and the truth to replace it:

....
....
....
....

Gauge your prayer life this month

We all have the tendency to forget to pray over certain areas of our lives. Use this gauge to help you identify areas that need a little bit more of your attention this month.
Head over to the 'scriptures to pray' section and choose a few scriptures to pray & declare.

GOVERNMENT

1 2 3 4 5 6 7 8 9 10

FAMILY

1 2 3 4 5 6 7 8 9 10

CHURCH

1 2 3 4 5 6 7 8 9 10

LIFE

1 2 3 4 5 6 7 8 9 10

THE LOST

1 2 3 4 5 6 7 8 9 10

MY NEEDS

1 2 3 4 5 6 7 8 9 10

Hopes & Dreams

DREAM WITH GOD IN MIND AND MAKE MARGIN FOR MIRACLES.

Government

I URGE, THEN, FIRST OF ALL,
THAT **PETITIONS**, **PRAYERS**, **INTERCESSION** AND **THANKSGIVING** BE MADE
FOR ALL PEOPLE—FOR KINGS AND ALL THOSE IN AUTHORITY, THAT WE MAY
LIVE PEACEFUL AND QUIET LIVES IN ALL GODLINESS AND HOLINESS. THIS IS
GOOD, AND PLEASES GOD OUR SAVIOR.
1 TIMOTHY 2:1-3 (NIV)

WHAT TO PRAY FOR:

WISE COUNSEL . TRUST IN GOD. PROTECTION . HOLY SPIRIT
GUIDANCE . COURAGE TO DO RIGHT . COMPASSIONATE
HEARTS . STRENGTH . DO GOD'S WILL . SALVATION

WHO TO PRAY FOR:

....
President

....
Governor

....
Mayor

....
Police Chief

....
Sheriff

....
City Leaders

....
Adopt-A-Cop

Here are six ways to pray for officers: pray they come to know Jesus Christ as their Savior. Pray for compassion in their hearts for the people they serve. Pray they would exhibit integrity, honesty and dedication. Pray for wisdom and understanding. Pray for their mental, emotional and physical health. Pray for their families.

Family

BEAR WITH EACH OTHER AND FORGIVE ONE ANOTHER IF ANY OF YOU
HAS A GRIEVANCE AGAINST SOMEONE. FORGIVE AS THE LORD
FORGAVE YOU. AND OVER ALL THESE VIRTUES PUT ON LOVE, WHICH
BINDS THEM ALL TOGETHER IN PERFECT UNITY.
COLOSSIANS 3:13-14 (NIV)

SPOUSE

CHILDREN

PARENTS/SIBLINGS

EXTENDED FAMILY

Church

YOU ALSO, AS LIVING STONES, ARE BEING BUILT UP AS A SPIRITUAL
HOUSE FOR A HOLY PRIESTHOOD, TO OFFER UP SPIRITUAL
SACRIFICES ACCEPTABLE TO GOD THROUGH JESUS CHRIST.
1 PETER 2:5 (NASB)

PASTOR(S)

LEADERSHIP

SMALL GROUP

MISSIONS

Life

I HAVE BEEN CRUCIFIED WITH CHRIST; IT IS NO LONGER I WHO LIVE,
BUT CHRIST LIVES IN ME; AND THE LIFE WHICH I NOW LIVE IN THE
FLESH I LIVE BY FAITH IN THE SON OF GOD, WHO LOVED ME AND
GAVE HIMSELF FOR ME.
GALATIANS 2:20 (NKJV)

EMPLOYER

EMPLOYEES/CO-WORKERS

MENTORS/TEACHERS

CLOSE FRIENDS

NEW FRIENDS

TEAMS I LEAD

The Lost

FRIENDS. NEIGHBORS. CO-WORKERS. PEOPLE YOU MEET. FAMILY.

....

A Prayer for those who need to know Jesus

Father,

I pray that you would draw my friends to Jesus today (John 6:44). Please bind the spirit that blinds their minds so that they may see the light of the gospel (2 Corinthians 4:4). I ask that the spirit of adoption would come upon them and that they would find freedom from fear and slavery to sin. I pray that your love would flood their minds and hearts. I ask that your love would cause them to cry out "Abba, Father," to you oh Lord! Father, I pray that they would experience an identity exchange from orphans to children of God today (Romans 3:15)! I ask that you would commission and orchestrate divine appointments with other Christians! You are the Lord of the Harvest and your word says that we are to ask you to send out workers. I come into agreement with your word right now (Matthew 9:38). Father, only you can give the Spirit of wisdom and of revelation in the knowledge of Jesus! I pray that you would release this amazing gift on their minds and hearts (Ephesians 1:17).

Finally Father, I pray that they would come to know what the length, and width, and height, and depth of Your amazing love! (Ephesians 3:18)

In Jesus name, Amen!

My Needs

BE ANXIOUS FOR NOTHING, BUT IN EVERYTHING BY PRAYER AND
SUPPLICATION, WITH THANKSGIVING, LET YOUR REQUESTS BE MADE
KNOWN TO GOD; AND THE PEACE OF GOD, WHICH SURPASSES ALL
UNDERSTANDING, WILL GUARD YOUR HEARTS AND MINDS THROUGH
CHRIST JESUS.
PHILIPPIANS 4:6-8 (NKJV)

PHYSICAL

RELATIONAL

FINANCIAL

SPIRITUAL

MENTAL/EMOTIONAL

MORE

Prayer Request

AND THIS IS THE CONFIDENCE THAT WE HAVE TOWARD HIM, THAT IF WE ASK
ANYTHING ACCORDING TO HIS WILL HE HEARS US. AND IF WE KNOW THAT HE
HEARS US IN WHATEVER WE ASK, WE KNOW THAT WE HAVE THE REQUESTS
THAT WE HAVE ASKED OF HIM.
1 JOHN 5:14-15 (ESV)

Prayer Request

FOR THE LORD GOD IS A SUN AND SHIELD: THE LORD WILL GIVE
GRACE AND GLORY: NO GOOD THING WILL HE WITHHOLD FROM THEM
THAT WALK UPRIGHTLY.
PSALM 84:11 (KJV)

DATE REQUESTED	DATE ANSWERED

Thank You!

NOW THANKS BE TO GOD WHO ALWAYS LEADS US IN TRIUMPH IN CHRIST, AND
THROUGH US DIFFUSES THE FRAGRANCE OF HIS KNOWLEDGE IN EVERY
PLACE. 2 CORINTHIANS 2:14 (NKJV)

1 ....
2 ....
3 ....
4 ....
5 ....
6 ....
7 ....
8 ....
9 ....
10 ....
11 ....
12 ....
13 ....
14 ....
15 ....
16 ....
17 ....
18 ....
19 ....
20 ....
21 ....
22 ....
23 ....
24 ....
25 ....
26 ....
27 ....
28 ....
29 ....
30 ....
31 ....

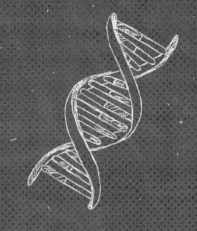

I am fearfully and wonderfully made.

"I praise you, for I am fearfully and wonderfully made. Wonderful are your works; my soul knows it very well."

Psalm 139:14 (esv)

Monthly Prayer Goals!

I praise you, for I am fearfully and wonderfully made.
Wonderful are your works; my soul knows it very well.
Psalm 139:14 (esv)

Memory verse:

....
....
....
....
....

Key words for this month:

....
....
....
....

Lies, shame or guilt you may be embracing and the truth to replace it:

....
....
....
....

Gauge your prayer life this month

We all have the tendency to forget to pray over certain areas
of our lives. Use this gauge to help you identify areas that
need a little bit more of your attention this month.
Head over to the 'scriptures to pray' section and choose a few
scriptures to pray & declare.

GOVERNMENT

1 2 3 4 5 6 7 8 9 10

LIFE

1 2 3 4 5 6 7 8 9 10

FAMILY

1 2 3 4 5 6 7 8 9 10

THE LOST

1 2 3 4 5 6 7 8 9 10

CHURCH

1 2 3 4 5 6 7 8 9 10

MY NEEDS

1 2 3 4 5 6 7 8 9 10

Hopes & Dreams

DREAM WITH GOD IN MIND AND MAKE MARGIN FOR MIRACLES.

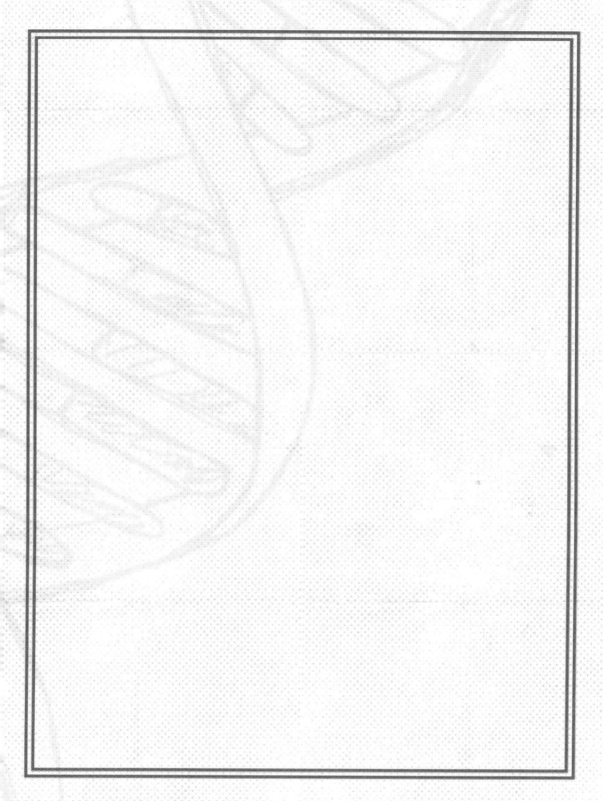

Government

I URGE, THEN, FIRST OF ALL,
THAT **PETITIONS**, **PRAYERS**, **INTERCESSION** AND **THANKSGIVING** BE MADE
FOR ALL PEOPLE—FOR KINGS AND ALL THOSE IN AUTHORITY, THAT WE MAY
LIVE PEACEFUL AND QUIET LIVES IN ALL GODLINESS AND HOLINESS. THIS IS
GOOD, AND PLEASES GOD OUR SAVIOR.
1 TIMOTHY 2:1-3 (NIV)

WHAT TO PRAY FOR:

WISE COUNSEL . TRUST IN GOD. PROTECTION . HOLY SPIRIT
GUIDANCE . COURAGE TO DO RIGHT . COMPASSIONATE
HEARTS . STRENGTH . DO GOD'S WILL . SALVATION

WHO TO PRAY FOR:

President

Governor

Mayor

Police Chief

Sheriff

City Leaders

Adopt-A-Cop

Here are six ways to pray for officers: pray they come to know Jesus Christ as their Savior. Pray for compassion in their hearts for the people they serve. Pray they would exhibit integrity, honesty and dedication. Pray for wisdom and understanding. Pray for their mental, emotional and physical health. Pray for their families.

Family

BEAR WITH EACH OTHER AND FORGIVE ONE ANOTHER IF ANY OF YOU
HAS A GRIEVANCE AGAINST SOMEONE. FORGIVE AS THE LORD
FORGAVE YOU. AND OVER ALL THESE VIRTUES PUT ON LOVE, WHICH
BINDS THEM ALL TOGETHER IN PERFECT UNITY.
COLOSSIANS 3:13-14 (NIV)

SPOUSE

CHILDREN

PARENTS/SIBLINGS

EXTENDED FAMILY

Church

YOU ALSO, AS LIVING STONES, ARE BEING BUILT UP AS A SPIRITUAL
HOUSE FOR A HOLY PRIESTHOOD, TO OFFER UP SPIRITUAL
SACRIFICES ACCEPTABLE TO GOD THROUGH JESUS CHRIST.
1 PETER 2:5 (NASB)

PASTOR(S)

LEADERSHIP

SMALL GROUP

MISSIONS

Life

I HAVE BEEN CRUCIFIED WITH CHRIST; IT IS NO LONGER I WHO LIVE, BUT CHRIST LIVES IN ME; AND THE LIFE WHICH I NOW LIVE IN THE FLESH I LIVE BY FAITH IN THE SON OF GOD, WHO LOVED ME AND GAVE HIMSELF FOR ME.
GALATIANS 2:20 (NKJV)

EMPLOYER

EMPLOYEES/CO-WORKERS

MENTORS/TEACHERS

CLOSE FRIENDS

NEW FRIENDS

TEAMS I LEAD

The Lost

TO OPEN THEIR EYES, SO THAT THEY MAY TURN FROM DARKNESS TO LIGHT AND FROM THE POWER OF SATAN TO GOD, THAT THEY MAY RECEIVE FORGIVENESS OF SINS AND A PLACE AMONG THOSE WHO ARE SANCTIFIED BY FAITH IN ME.
ACTS 26:18 (NKJV)

FRIENDS. NEIGHBORS. CO-WORKERS. PEOPLE YOU MEET. FAMILY.

....

A Prayer for those who need to know Jesus...

Father,

I pray that you would draw my friends to Jesus today (John 6:44). Please bind the spirit that blinds their minds so that they may see the light of the gospel (2 Corinthians 4:4). I ask that the spirit of adoption would come upon them and that they would find freedom from fear and slavery to sin. I pray that your love would flood their minds and hearts. I ask that your love would cause them to cry out "Abba, Father," to you oh Lord! Father, I pray that they would experience an identity exchange from orphans to children of God today (Romans 3:15)! I ask that you would commission and orchestrate divine appointments with other Christians! You are the Lord of the Harvest and your word says that we are to ask you to send out workers. I come into agreement with your word right now (Matthew 9:38). Father, only you can give the Spirit of wisdom and of revelation in the knowledge of Jesus! I pray that you would release this amazing gift on their minds and hearts (Ephesians 1:17).

Finally Father, I pray that they would come to know what the length, and width, and height, and depth of Your amazing love! (Ephesians 3:18)

In Jesus name, Amen!

My Needs

BE ANXIOUS FOR NOTHING, BUT IN EVERYTHING BY PRAYER AND SUPPLICATION, WITH THANKSGIVING, LET YOUR REQUESTS BE MADE KNOWN TO GOD; AND THE PEACE OF GOD, WHICH SURPASSES ALL UNDERSTANDING, WILL GUARD YOUR HEARTS AND MINDS THROUGH CHRIST JESUS.
PHILIPPIANS 4:6-8 (NKJV)

PHYSICAL

RELATIONAL

FINANCIAL

SPIRITUAL

MENTAL/EMOTIONAL

MORE

Prayer Request

AND THIS IS THE CONFIDENCE THAT WE HAVE TOWARD HIM, THAT IF WE ASK
ANYTHING ACCORDING TO HIS WILL HE HEARS US. AND IF WE KNOW THAT HE
HEARS US IN WHATEVER WE ASK, WE KNOW THAT WE HAVE THE REQUESTS
THAT WE HAVE ASKED OF HIM.
1 JOHN 5:14-15 (ESV)

Prayer Request

FOR THE LORD GOD IS A SUN AND SHIELD: THE LORD WILL GIVE
GRACE AND GLORY: NO GOOD THING WILL HE WITHHOLD FROM THEM
THAT WALK UPRIGHTLY.
PSALM 84:11 (KJV)

DATE REQUESTED   DATE ANSWERED

....
....
....
....
....
....
....
....
....
....
....
....
....
....
....
....
....
....
....
....
....
....
....

Thank You!

NOW THANKS BE TO GOD WHO ALWAYS LEADS US IN TRIUMPH IN CHRIST, AND THROUGH US DIFFUSES THE FRAGRANCE OF HIS KNOWLEDGE IN EVERY PLACE. 2 CORINTHIANS 2:14 (NKJV)

1 ....
2 ....
3 ....
4 ....
5 ....
6 ....
7 ....
8 ....
9 ....
10 ....
11 ....
12 ....
13 ....
14 ....
15 ....
16 ....
17 ....
18 ....
19 ....
20 ....
21 ....
22 ....
23 ....
24 ....
25 ....
26 ....
27 ....
28 ....
29 ....
30 ....
31 ....

*My identity was given to me
before I was born*

"Before I formed you in the womb I knew
you, and before you were born I consecrated you; I appointed you a prophet to the
nations."

Jeremiah 1:5 (esv)

Monthly Prayer Goals!

Before I formed you in the womb I knew you, and before you were born I consecrated you; I appointed you a prophet to the nations. Jeremiah 1:5 (esv)

Memory verse:
....
....
....
....
....

Key words for this month:
....
....
....
....

Lies, shame or guilt you may be embracing and the truth to replace it:
....
....
....
....

Gauge your prayer life this month

We all have the tendency to forget to pray over certain areas of our lives. Use this gauge to help you identify areas that need a little bit more of your attention this month.
Head over to the 'scriptures to pray' section and choose a few scriptures to pray & declare.

GOVERNMENT

1 2 3 4 5 6 7 8 9 10

FAMILY

1 2 3 4 5 6 7 8 9 10

CHURCH

1 2 3 4 5 6 7 8 9 10

LIFE

1 2 3 4 5 6 7 8 9 10

THE LOST

1 2 3 4 5 6 7 8 9 10

MY NEEDS

1 2 3 4 5 6 7 8 9 10

Hopes & Dreams

DREAM WITH GOD IN MIND AND MAKE MARGIN FOR MIRACLES.

Government

I URGE, THEN, FIRST OF ALL,
THAT **PETITIONS, PRAYERS, INTERCESSION** AND **THANKSGIVING** BE MADE
FOR ALL PEOPLE—FOR KINGS AND ALL THOSE IN AUTHORITY, THAT WE MAY
LIVE PEACEFUL AND QUIET LIVES IN ALL GODLINESS AND HOLINESS. THIS IS
GOOD, AND PLEASES GOD OUR SAVIOR.
1 TIMOTHY 2:1-3 (NIV)

WHAT TO PRAY FOR:

WISE COUNSEL . TRUST IN GOD . PROTECTION . HOLY SPIRIT
GUIDANCE . COURAGE TO DO RIGHT . COMPASSIONATE
HEARTS . STRENGTH . DO GOD'S WILL . SALVATION

WHO TO PRAY FOR:

President

Governor

Mayor

Police Chief

Sheriff

City Leaders

Adopt-A-Cop

Here are six ways to pray for officers: pray they come to know Jesus Christ as their Savior. Pray for compassion in their hearts for the people they serve. Pray they would exhibit integrity, honesty and dedication. Pray for wisdom and understanding. Pray for their mental, emotional and physical health. Pray for their families.

Family

BEAR WITH EACH OTHER AND FORGIVE ONE ANOTHER IF ANY OF YOU
HAS A GRIEVANCE AGAINST SOMEONE. FORGIVE AS THE LORD
FORGAVE YOU. AND OVER ALL THESE VIRTUES PUT ON LOVE, WHICH
BINDS THEM ALL TOGETHER IN PERFECT UNITY.
COLOSSIANS 3:13-14 (NIV)

SPOUSE

CHILDREN

PARENTS/SIBLINGS

EXTENDED FAMILY

Church

YOU ALSO, AS LIVING STONES, ARE BEING BUILT UP AS A SPIRITUAL
HOUSE FOR A HOLY PRIESTHOOD, TO OFFER UP SPIRITUAL
SACRIFICES ACCEPTABLE TO GOD THROUGH JESUS CHRIST.
1 PETER 2:5 (NASB)

PASTOR(S)

LEADERSHIP

SMALL GROUP

MISSIONS

Life

I HAVE BEEN CRUCIFIED WITH CHRIST; IT IS NO LONGER I WHO LIVE,
BUT CHRIST LIVES IN ME; AND THE LIFE WHICH I NOW LIVE IN THE
FLESH I LIVE BY FAITH IN THE SON OF GOD, WHO LOVED ME AND
GAVE HIMSELF FOR ME.
GALATIANS 2:20 (NKJV)

EMPLOYER

EMPLOYEES/CO-WORKERS

MENTORS/TEACHERS

CLOSE FRIENDS

NEW FRIENDS

TEAMS I LEAD

The Lost

TO OPEN THEIR EYES, SO THAT THEY MAY TURN FROM DARKNESS TO LIGHT AND FROM THE POWER OF SATAN TO GOD, THAT THEY MAY RECEIVE FORGIVENESS OF SINS AND A PLACE AMONG THOSE WHO ARE SANCTIFIED BY FAITH IN ME.
ACTS 26:18 (NKJV)

FRIENDS. NEIGHBORS. CO-WORKERS. PEOPLE YOU MEET. FAMILY.

....

A Prayer for those who need to know Jesus.

Father,

I pray that you would draw my friends to Jesus today (John 6:44). Please bind the spirit that blinds their minds so that they may see the light of the gospel (2 Corinthians 4:4). I ask that the spirit of adoption would come upon them and that they would find freedom from fear and slavery to sin. I pray that your love would flood their minds and hearts. I ask that your love would cause them to cry out "Abba, Father," to you oh Lord! Father, I pray that they would experience an identity exchange from orphans to children of God today (Romans 3:15)! I ask that you would commission and orchestrate divine appointments with other Christians! You are the Lord of the Harvest and your word says that we are to ask you to send out workers. I come into agreement with your word right now (Matthew 9:38). Father, only you can give the Spirit of wisdom and of revelation in the knowledge of Jesus! I pray that you would release this amazing gift on their minds and hearts (Ephesians 1:17).

Finally Father, I pray that they would come to know what the length, and width, and height, and depth of Your amazing love! (Ephesians 3:18)

In Jesus name, Amen!

My Needs

BE ANXIOUS FOR NOTHING, BUT IN EVERYTHING BY PRAYER AND
SUPPLICATION, WITH THANKSGIVING, LET YOUR REQUESTS BE MADE
KNOWN TO GOD; AND THE PEACE OF GOD, WHICH SURPASSES ALL
UNDERSTANDING, WILL GUARD YOUR HEARTS AND MINDS THROUGH
CHRIST JESUS.
PHILIPPIANS 4:6-8 (NKJV)

PHYSICAL

RELATIONAL

FINANCIAL

SPIRITUAL

MENTAL/EMOTIONAL

MORE

Prayer Request

AND THIS IS THE CONFIDENCE THAT WE HAVE TOWARD HIM, THAT IF WE ASK
ANYTHING ACCORDING TO HIS WILL HE HEARS US. AND IF WE KNOW THAT HE
HEARS US IN WHATEVER WE ASK, WE KNOW THAT WE HAVE THE REQUESTS
THAT WE HAVE ASKED OF HIM.
1 JOHN 5:14-15 (ESV)

Prayer Request

FOR THE LORD GOD IS A SUN AND SHIELD: THE LORD WILL GIVE
GRACE AND GLORY: NO GOOD THING WILL HE WITHHOLD FROM THEM
THAT WALK UPRIGHTLY.
PSALM 84:11 (KJV)

DATE REQUESTED	DATE ANSWERED

Thank You!

NOW THANKS BE TO GOD WHO ALWAYS LEADS US IN TRIUMPH IN CHRIST, AND THROUGH US DIFFUSES THE FRAGRANCE OF HIS KNOWLEDGE IN EVERY PLACE. 2 CORINTHIANS 2:14 (NKJV)

1 ....
2 ....
3 ....
4 ....
5 ....
6 ....
7 ....
8 ....
9 ....
10 ....
11 ....
12 ....
13 ....
14 ....
15 ....
16 ....
17 ....
18 ....
19 ....
20 ....
21 ....
22 ....
23 ....
24 ....
25 ....
26 ....
27 ....
28 ....
29 ....
30 ....
31 ....

Remember that day? I was there with you.

"You saw me before I was born. Every day
of my life was recorded in your book.
Every moment was laid out before a single
day had passed."

Psalm 139:16 (nlt)

Monthly Prayer Goals!

You saw me before I was born. Every day of my life was recorded in your book. Every moment was laid out before a single day had passed. Psalm 139:16 (Nlt)

Memory verse:

....
....
....
....
....

Key words for this month:

....
....
....
....

Lies, shame or guilt you may be embracing and the truth to replace it:

....
....
....
....

Gauge your prayer life this month

We all have the tendency to forget to pray over certain areas of our lives. Use this gauge to help you identify areas that need a little bit more of your attention this month.
Head over to the 'scriptures to pray' section and choose a few scriptures to pray & declare.

GOVERNMENT

1 2 3 4 5 6 7 8 9 10

FAMILY

1 2 3 4 5 6 7 8 9 10

CHURCH

1 2 3 4 5 6 7 8 9 10

LIFE

1 2 3 4 5 6 7 8 9 10

THE LOST

1 2 3 4 5 6 7 8 9 10

MY NEEDS

1 2 3 4 5 6 7 8 9 10

Hopes & Dreams

DREAM WITH GOD IN MIND AND MAKE MARGIN FOR MIRACLES.

Government

I URGE, THEN, FIRST OF ALL,
THAT **PETITIONS, PRAYERS, INTERCESSION** AND **THANKSGIVING** BE MADE
FOR ALL PEOPLE—FOR KINGS AND ALL THOSE IN AUTHORITY, THAT WE MAY
LIVE PEACEFUL AND QUIET LIVES IN ALL GODLINESS AND HOLINESS. THIS IS
GOOD, AND PLEASES GOD OUR SAVIOR.
1 TIMOTHY 2:1-3 (NIV)

WHAT TO PRAY FOR:

WISE COUNSEL . TRUST IN GOD. PROTECTION . HOLY SPIRIT
GUIDANCE . COURAGE TO DO RIGHT . COMPASSIONATE
HEARTS . STRENGTH . DO GOD'S WILL . SALVATION

WHO TO PRAY FOR:

....

President

....

Governor

....

Mayor

....

Police Chief

....

Sheriff

....

City Leaders

....

Adopt-A-Cop

Here are six ways to pray for officers: pray they come to know Jesus Christ as their Savior. Pray
for compassion in their hearts for the people they serve. Pray they would exhibit integrity,
honesty and dedication. Pray for wisdom and understanding. Pray for their mental, emotional
and physical health. Pray for their families.

Family

BEAR WITH EACH OTHER AND FORGIVE ONE ANOTHER IF ANY OF YOU
HAS A GRIEVANCE AGAINST SOMEONE. FORGIVE AS THE LORD
FORGAVE YOU. AND OVER ALL THESE VIRTUES PUT ON LOVE, WHICH
BINDS THEM ALL TOGETHER IN PERFECT UNITY.
COLOSSIANS 3:13-14 (NIV)

SPOUSE

CHILDREN

PARENTS/SIBLINGS

EXTENDED FAMILY

Church

YOU ALSO, AS LIVING STONES, ARE BEING BUILT UP AS A SPIRITUAL
HOUSE FOR A HOLY PRIESTHOOD, TO OFFER UP SPIRITUAL
SACRIFICES ACCEPTABLE TO GOD THROUGH JESUS CHRIST.
1 PETER 2:5 (NASB)

PASTOR(S)

LEADERSHIP

SMALL GROUP

MISSIONS

Life

I HAVE BEEN CRUCIFIED WITH CHRIST; IT IS NO LONGER I WHO LIVE,
BUT CHRIST LIVES IN ME; AND THE LIFE WHICH I NOW LIVE IN THE
FLESH I LIVE BY FAITH IN THE SON OF GOD, WHO LOVED ME AND
GAVE HIMSELF FOR ME.
GALATIANS 2:20 (NKJV)

EMPLOYER

EMPLOYEES/CO-WORKERS

MENTORS/TEACHERS

CLOSE FRIENDS

NEW FRIENDS

TEAMS I LEAD

The Lost

TO OPEN THEIR EYES, SO THAT THEY MAY TURN FROM DARKNESS TO
LIGHT AND FROM THE POWER OF SATAN TO GOD, THAT THEY MAY
RECEIVE FORGIVENESS OF SINS AND A PLACE AMONG THOSE WHO
ARE SANCTIFIED BY FAITH IN ME.
ACTS 26:18 (NKJV)

FRIENDS. NEIGHBORS. CO-WORKERS. PEOPLE YOU MEET. FAMILY.

....

A Prayer for those who need to know Jesus.

Father,

I pray that you would draw my friends to Jesus today
(John 6:44). Please bind the spirit that blinds their minds so
that they may see the light of the gospel (2 Corinthians 4:4). I
ask that the spirit of adoption would come upon them and that
they would find freedom from fear and slavery to sin. I pray
that your love would flood their minds and hearts. I ask that
your love would cause them to cry out "Abba, Father," to you
oh Lord! Father, I pray that they would experience an identity
exchange from orphans to children of God today (Romans
3:15)! I ask that you would commission and orchestrate divine
appointments with other Christians! You are the Lord of the
Harvest and your word says that we are to ask you to send out
workers. I come into agreement with your word right now
(Matthew 9:38). Father, only you can give the Spirit of wisdom
and of revelation in the knowledge of Jesus! I pray that you
would release this amazing gift on their minds and hearts
(Ephesians 1:17).

Finally Father, I pray that they would come to know what the
length, and width, and height, and depth of Your amazing
love! (Ephesians 3:18)

In Jesus name, Amen!

My Needs

BE ANXIOUS FOR NOTHING, BUT IN EVERYTHING BY PRAYER AND
SUPPLICATION, WITH THANKSGIVING, LET YOUR REQUESTS BE MADE
KNOWN TO GOD; AND THE PEACE OF GOD, WHICH SURPASSES ALL
UNDERSTANDING, WILL GUARD YOUR HEARTS AND MINDS THROUGH
CHRIST JESUS.
PHILIPPIANS 4:6-8 (NKJV)

PHYSICAL

RELATIONAL

FINANCIAL

SPIRITUAL

MENTAL/EMOTIONAL

MORE

Prayer Request

AND THIS IS THE CONFIDENCE THAT WE HAVE TOWARD HIM, THAT IF WE ASK ANYTHING ACCORDING TO HIS WILL HE HEARS US. AND IF WE KNOW THAT HE HEARS US IN WHATEVER WE ASK, WE KNOW THAT WE HAVE THE REQUESTS THAT WE HAVE ASKED OF HIM.
1 JOHN 5:14-15 (ESV)

Prayer Request

FOR THE LORD GOD IS A SUN AND SHIELD: THE LORD WILL GIVE
GRACE AND GLORY: NO GOOD THING WILL HE WITHHOLD FROM THEM
THAT WALK UPRIGHTLY.
PSALM 84:11 (KJV)

DATE REQUESTED	DATE ANSWERED
....	....
....	....
....	....
....	....
....	....
....	....
....	....
....	....
....	....
....	....
....	....
....	....
....	....
....	....
....	....
....	....
....	....
....	....
....	....
....	....
....	....
....	....
....	....
....	....
....	....
....	....
....	....

Thank You!

NOW THANKS BE TO GOD WHO ALWAYS LEADS US IN TRIUMPH IN CHRIST, AND
THROUGH US DIFFUSES THE FRAGRANCE OF HIS KNOWLEDGE IN EVERY
PLACE. 2 CORINTHIANS 2:14 (NKJV)

1 ....
2 ....
3 ....
4 ....
5 ....
6 ....
7 ....
8 ....
9 ....
10 ....
11 ....
12 ....
13 ....
14 ....
15 ....
16 ....
17 ....
18 ....
19 ....
20 ....
21 ....
22 ....
23 ....
24 ....
25 ....
26 ....
27 ....
28 ....
29 ....
30 ....
31 ....

Don't forget to remember

"The Lord your God will soon bring you into the land he swore to give you when he made a vow to your ancestors Abraham, Isaac, and Jacob. It is a land with large, prosperous cities that you did not build. The houses will be richly stocked with goods you did not produce. You will draw water from cisterns you did not dig, and you will eat from vineyards and olive trees you did not plant. When you have eaten your fill in this land, be careful not to forget the Lord, who rescued you from slavery in the land of Egypt."

Deuteronomy 6: 10-12 (NLT)

Monthly Prayer Goals!

Be careful not to forget the Lord, who rescued you from slavery in the land of Egypt.
Deuteronomy 6:10-18 (nlt)

Memory verse:

....
....
....
....
....

Key words for this month:

....
....
....
....

Lies, shame or guilt you may be embracing and the truth to replace it:

....
....
....
....

Gauge your prayer life this month

We all have the tendency to forget to pray over certain areas
of our lives. Use this gauge to help you identify areas that
need a little bit more of your attention this month.
Head over to the 'scriptures to pray' section and choose a few
scriptures to pray & declare.

GOVERNMENT

1 2 3 4 5 6 7 8 9 10

FAMILY

1 2 3 4 5 6 7 8 9 10

CHURCH

1 2 3 4 5 6 7 8 9 10

LIFE

1 2 3 4 5 6 7 8 9 10

THE LOST

1 2 3 4 5 6 7 8 9 10

MY NEEDS

1 2 3 4 5 6 7 8 9 10

Hopes & Dreams

DREAM WITH GOD IN MIND AND MAKE MARGIN FOR MIRACLES.

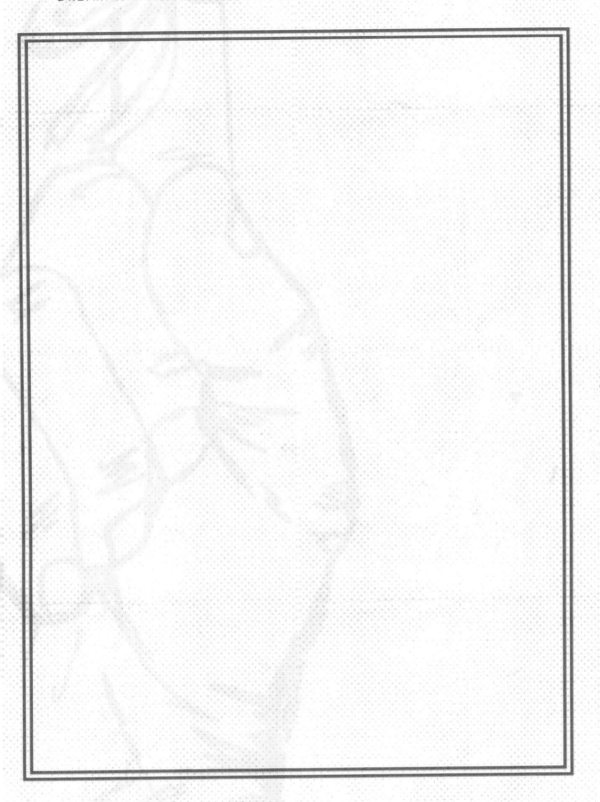

Government

I URGE, THEN, FIRST OF ALL,
THAT **PETITIONS, PRAYERS, INTERCESSION** AND **THANKSGIVING** BE MADE
FOR ALL PEOPLE—FOR KINGS AND ALL THOSE IN AUTHORITY, THAT WE MAY
LIVE PEACEFUL AND QUIET LIVES IN ALL GODLINESS AND HOLINESS. THIS IS
GOOD, AND PLEASES GOD OUR SAVIOR.
1 TIMOTHY 2:1-3 (NIV)

WHAT TO PRAY FOR:

WISE COUNSEL . TRUST IN GOD. PROTECTION . HOLY SPIRIT
GUIDANCE . COURAGE TO DO RIGHT . COMPASSIONATE
HEARTS . STRENGTH . DO GOD'S WILL . SALVATION

WHO TO PRAY FOR:

....
President

....
Governor

....
Mayor

....
Police Chief

....
Sheriff

....
City Leaders

....
Adopt-A-Cop

Here are six ways to pray for officers: pray they come to know Jesus Christ as their Savior. Pray
for compassion in their hearts for the people they serve. Pray they would exhibit integrity,
honesty and dedication. Pray for wisdom and understanding. Pray for their mental, emotional
and physical health. Pray for their families.

Family

BEAR WITH EACH OTHER AND FORGIVE ONE ANOTHER IF ANY OF YOU HAS A GRIEVANCE AGAINST SOMEONE. FORGIVE AS THE LORD FORGAVE YOU. AND OVER ALL THESE VIRTUES PUT ON LOVE, WHICH BINDS THEM ALL TOGETHER IN PERFECT UNITY.
COLOSSIANS 3:13-14 (NIV)

SPOUSE

CHILDREN

PARENTS/SIBLINGS

EXTENDED FAMILY

Church

YOU ALSO, AS LIVING STONES, ARE BEING BUILT UP AS A SPIRITUAL
HOUSE FOR A HOLY PRIESTHOOD, TO OFFER UP SPIRITUAL
SACRIFICES ACCEPTABLE TO GOD THROUGH JESUS CHRIST.
1 PETER 2:5 (NASB)

PASTOR(S)

LEADERSHIP

SMALL GROUP

MISSIONS

Life

I HAVE BEEN CRUCIFIED WITH CHRIST; IT IS NO LONGER I WHO LIVE,
BUT CHRIST LIVES IN ME; AND THE LIFE WHICH I NOW LIVE IN THE
FLESH I LIVE BY FAITH IN THE SON OF GOD, WHO LOVED ME AND
GAVE HIMSELF FOR ME.
GALATIANS 2:20 (NKJV)

EMPLOYER

EMPLOYEES/CO-WORKERS

MENTORS/TEACHERS

CLOSE FRIENDS

NEW FRIENDS

TEAMS I LEAD

The Lost

TO OPEN THEIR EYES, SO THAT THEY MAY TURN FROM DARKNESS TO LIGHT AND FROM THE POWER OF SATAN TO GOD, THAT THEY MAY RECEIVE FORGIVENESS OF SINS AND A PLACE AMONG THOSE WHO ARE SANCTIFIED BY FAITH IN ME.

ACTS 26:18 (NKJV)

FRIENDS. NEIGHBORS. CO-WORKERS. PEOPLE YOU MEET. FAMILY.

....

A Prayer for those who need to know Jesus.

Father,

I pray that you would draw my friends to Jesus today (John 6:44). Please bind the spirit that blinds their minds so that they may see the light of the gospel (2 Corinthians 4:4). I ask that the spirit of adoption would come upon them and that they would find freedom from fear and slavery to sin. I pray that your love would flood their minds and hearts. I ask that your love would cause them to cry out "Abba, Father," to you oh Lord! Father, I pray that they would experience an identity exchange from orphans to children of God today (Romans 3:15)! I ask that you would commission and orchestrate divine appointments with other Christians! You are the Lord of the Harvest and your word says that we are to ask you to send out workers. I come into agreement with your word right now (Matthew 9:38). Father, only you can give the Spirit of wisdom and of revelation in the knowledge of Jesus! I pray that you would release this amazing gift on their minds and hearts (Ephesians 1:17).

Finally Father, I pray that they would come to know what the length, and width, and height, and depth of Your amazing love! (Ephesians 3:18)

In Jesus name, Amen!

My needs

BE ANXIOUS FOR NOTHING, BUT IN EVERYTHING BY PRAYER AND SUPPLICATION, WITH THANKSGIVING, LET YOUR REQUESTS BE MADE KNOWN TO GOD; AND THE PEACE OF GOD, WHICH SURPASSES ALL UNDERSTANDING, WILL GUARD YOUR HEARTS AND MINDS THROUGH CHRIST JESUS.
PHILIPPIANS 4:6-8 (NKJV)

PHYSICAL

RELATIONAL

FINANCIAL

SPIRITUAL

MENTAL/EMOTIONAL

MORE

Prayer Request

AND THIS IS THE CONFIDENCE THAT WE HAVE TOWARD HIM, THAT IF WE ASK ANYTHING ACCORDING TO HIS WILL HE HEARS US. AND IF WE KNOW THAT HE HEARS US IN WHATEVER WE ASK, WE KNOW THAT WE HAVE THE REQUESTS THAT WE HAVE ASKED OF HIM.
1 JOHN 5:14-15 (ESV)

Prayer Request

FOR THE LORD GOD IS A SUN AND SHIELD: THE LORD WILL GIVE
GRACE AND GLORY: NO GOOD THING WILL HE WITHHOLD FROM THEM
THAT WALK UPRIGHTLY.
PSALM 84:11 (KJV)

DATE REQUESTED

DATE ANSWERED

Thank You!

NOW THANKS BE TO GOD WHO ALWAYS LEADS US IN TRIUMPH IN CHRIST, AND THROUGH US DIFFUSES THE FRAGRANCE OF HIS KNOWLEDGE IN EVERY PLACE. 2 CORINTHIANS 2:14 (NKJV)

1 ....
2 ....
3 ....
4 ....
5 ....
6 ....
7 ....
8 ....
9 ....
10 ....
11 ....
12 ....
13 ....
14 ....
15 ....
16 ....
17 ....
18 ....
19 ....
20 ....
21 ....
22 ....
23 ....
24 ....
25 ....
26 ....
27 ....
28 ....
29 ....
30 ....
31 ....

The angel of the Lord encamps around you.

The angel of the Lord encamps around those who fear Him, and rescues them.

Psalm 34:7 (nasb)

Monthly Prayer Goals!

*The angel of the LORD encamps around those who fear
Him, and rescues them.*
Psalm 34:7 (Nasb)

Memory verse:

....
....
....
....
....

Key words for this month:

....
....
....
....

Lies, shame or guilt you may be embracing and the truth to replace it:

....
....
....
....

Gauge your prayer life this month

We all have the tendency to forget to pray over certain areas
of our lives. Use this gauge to help you identify areas that
need a little bit more of your attention this month.
Head over to the 'scriptures to pray' section and choose a few
scriptures to pray & declare.

GOVERNMENT

1 2 3 4 5 6 7 8 9 10

FAMILY

1 2 3 4 5 6 7 8 9 10

CHURCH

1 2 3 4 5 6 7 8 9 10

LIFE

1 2 3 4 5 6 7 8 9 10

THE LOST

1 2 3 4 5 6 7 8 9 10

MY NEEDS

1 2 3 4 5 6 7 8 9 10

Hopes & Dreams

DREAM WITH GOD IN MIND AND MAKE MARGIN FOR MIRACLES.

Government

I URGE, THEN, FIRST OF ALL,
THAT **PETITIONS, PRAYERS, INTERCESSION** AND **THANKSGIVING** BE MADE
FOR ALL PEOPLE—FOR KINGS AND ALL THOSE IN AUTHORITY, THAT WE MAY
LIVE PEACEFUL AND QUIET LIVES IN ALL GODLINESS AND HOLINESS. THIS IS
GOOD, AND PLEASES GOD OUR SAVIOR.
1 TIMOTHY 2:1-3 (NIV)

W H A T   T O   P R A Y   F O R :

WISE COUNSEL . TRUST IN GOD. PROTECTION . HOLY SPIRIT
GUIDANCE . COURAGE TO DO RIGHT . COMPASSIONATE
HEARTS . STRENGTH . DO GOD'S WILL . SALVATION

W H O   T O   P R A Y   F O R :

President

Governor

Mayor

Police Chief

Sheriff

City Leaders

Adopt-A-Cop

Here are six ways to pray for officers: pray they come to know Jesus Christ as their Savior. Pray for compassion in their hearts for the people they serve. Pray they would exhibit integrity, honesty and dedication. Pray for wisdom and understanding. Pray for their mental, emotional and physical health. Pray for their families.

Family

BEAR WITH EACH OTHER AND FORGIVE ONE ANOTHER IF ANY OF YOU
HAS A GRIEVANCE AGAINST SOMEONE. FORGIVE AS THE LORD
FORGAVE YOU. AND OVER ALL THESE VIRTUES PUT ON LOVE, WHICH
BINDS THEM ALL TOGETHER IN PERFECT UNITY.
COLOSSIANS 3:13-14 (NIV)

SPOUSE

CHILDREN

PARENTS/SIBLINGS

EXTENDED FAMILY

Church

YOU ALSO, AS LIVING STONES, ARE BEING BUILT UP AS A SPIRITUAL
HOUSE FOR A HOLY PRIESTHOOD, TO OFFER UP SPIRITUAL
SACRIFICES ACCEPTABLE TO GOD THROUGH JESUS CHRIST.
1 PETER 2:5 (NASB)

PASTOR(S)

LEADERSHIP

SMALL GROUP

MISSIONS

Life

I HAVE BEEN CRUCIFIED WITH CHRIST; IT IS NO LONGER I WHO LIVE,
BUT CHRIST LIVES IN ME; AND THE LIFE WHICH I NOW LIVE IN THE
FLESH I LIVE BY FAITH IN THE SON OF GOD, WHO LOVED ME AND
GAVE HIMSELF FOR ME.
GALATIANS 2:20 (NKJV)

EMPLOYER

EMPLOYEES/CO-WORKERS

MENTORS/TEACHERS

CLOSE FRIENDS

NEW FRIENDS

TEAMS I LEAD

The Lost

TO OPEN THEIR EYES, SO THAT THEY MAY TURN FROM DARKNESS TO LIGHT AND FROM THE POWER OF SATAN TO GOD, THAT THEY MAY RECEIVE FORGIVENESS OF SINS AND A PLACE AMONG THOSE WHO ARE SANCTIFIED BY FAITH IN ME.
ACTS 26:18 (NKJV)

FRIENDS. NEIGHBORS. CO-WORKERS. PEOPLE YOU MEET. FAMILY.

....

A Prayer for those who need to know Jesus

Father,

I pray that you would draw my friends to Jesus today (John 6:44). Please bind the spirit that blinds their minds so that they may see the light of the gospel (2 Corinthians 4:4). I ask that the spirit of adoption would come upon them and that they would find freedom from fear and slavery to sin. I pray that your love would flood their minds and hearts. I ask that your love would cause them to cry out "Abba, Father," to you oh Lord! Father, I pray that they would experience an identity exchange from orphans to children of God today (Romans 3:15)! I ask that you would commission and orchestrate divine appointments with other Christians! You are the Lord of the Harvest and your word says that we are to ask you to send out workers. I come into agreement with your word right now (Matthew 9:38). Father, only you can give the Spirit of wisdom and of revelation in the knowledge of Jesus! I pray that you would release this amazing gift on their minds and hearts (Ephesians 1:17).

Finally Father, I pray that they would come to know what the length, and width, and height, and depth of Your amazing love! (Ephesians 3:18)

In Jesus name, Amen!

My Needs

BE ANXIOUS FOR NOTHING, BUT IN EVERYTHING BY PRAYER AND
SUPPLICATION, WITH THANKSGIVING, LET YOUR REQUESTS BE MADE
KNOWN TO GOD; AND THE PEACE OF GOD, WHICH SURPASSES ALL
UNDERSTANDING, WILL GUARD YOUR HEARTS AND MINDS THROUGH
CHRIST JESUS.
PHILIPPIANS 4:6-8 (NKJV)

PHYSICAL

RELATIONAL

FINANCIAL

SPIRITUAL

MENTAL/EMOTIONAL

MORE

Prayer Request

AND THIS IS THE CONFIDENCE THAT WE HAVE TOWARD HIM, THAT IF WE ASK
ANYTHING ACCORDING TO HIS WILL HE HEARS US. AND IF WE KNOW THAT HE
HEARS US IN WHATEVER WE ASK, WE KNOW THAT WE HAVE THE REQUESTS
THAT WE HAVE ASKED OF HIM.
1 JOHN 5:14-15 (ESV)

Prayer Request

FOR THE LORD GOD IS A SUN AND SHIELD: THE LORD WILL GIVE
GRACE AND GLORY: NO GOOD THING WILL HE WITHHOLD FROM THEM
THAT WALK UPRIGHTLY.
PSALM 84:11 (KJV)

DATE REQUESTED	DATE ANSWERED

Thank You!

NOW THANKS BE TO GOD WHO ALWAYS LEADS US IN TRIUMPH IN CHRIST, AND THROUGH US DIFFUSES THE FRAGRANCE OF HIS KNOWLEDGE IN EVERY PLACE. 2 CORINTHIANS 2:14 (NKJV)

1 ....
2 ....
3 ....
4 ....
5 ....
6 ....
7 ....
8 ....
9 ....
10 ....
11 ....
12 ....
13 ....
14 ....
15 ....
16 ....
17 ....
18 ....
19 ....
20 ....
21 ....
22 ....
23 ....
24 ....
25 ....
26 ....
27 ....
28 ....
29 ....
30 ....
31 ....

NOTES

Chapter 6

Silk, Danny. "The Trust Cycle". *Keep Your Love On!.* Loving On Purpose, 2013, pp. 112-113

Made in the USA
Columbia, SC
02 October 2021